MEDICAL INTUITION AND MUSCLE TESTING:

It's Coming, Don't Get Left Behind

Patrick Dougherty, DC

Contributions by:
Charles Lightwalker Lasol

MEDICAL INTUITION AND MUSCLE TESTING:

It's Coming, Don't Get Left Behind

By Patrick Dougherty DC, with contributions by,

Charles Lightwalker Lasol

Published by Chiropractic Lifecenter Inc Publishing

2110 North Washington Street Suite One

Spokane WA 99205

Books may be purchased in quantity and/or special sales by contacting the publisher, Chiropractic Lifecenter Inc at 2110 North Washington Street Suite One, Spokane WA 99205. 509-844-4206, by fax 509-327-1244 or by email at clcpcd@outlook.com

Published by: Chiropractic Lifecenter Inc Spoakne WA

Cover Design by Doug Cristafir, Radiantarts.com

Editing and proofreading by

Formatted by

Library of Congress Control Number:

ISBN: 978-0-9893606-4-7

1.Spirituality   2. Self Help   3. New Age   4. Metaphysical

First Edition

First Printing September 2021

TABLE OF CONTENTS

Other Books by Patrick Dougherty DC

Quantum Healing: The Synergy of Chiropractic and Reiki
With Charles Lightwalker Lasol

Do You Wanna Get Better?
The Future of Health Care

ACKNOWLEDGMENTS

I have written previously, I believe there are no original thoughts in this world. We are heavily influenced by all we have experienced. Our thoughts are shaped by the thoughts of those who came before us. Or, if we take the quantum viewpoint, everything exists simultaneously, and we have instant access when we allow ourselves to listen.

Either way I acknowledge I have been influenced by many and their influence has shaped the words in this book. Some of the most influential thinkers for me have been Donnie Epstein DC, John De Martini DC, Bruce Lipton, candace Pert PhD, Norman Doidge FRCPC, and James Oschmann PhD,

On a local personal level, several people I met only because I moved to Spokane 17 years ago are co-author Charles Lightwalker Lasol, Candess Campbell PhD, James Barfoot, and the sadly departed James Funke LICSW. Conversations with them have helped me expand and delve into the hidden world that is so much a part of Medical Intuition. This is the second book cover that Doug Cristafir has created for me. I trust his vision completely to capture the spirit I seek. Doug can be reached at Radiantarts.com

Finally, this book is dedicated to all who read it. You are a source of life for me. You are part of a transition to the healing of this world. There will be an inevitable transition from the many harmful practices that allopathic medicine embraces to a healthier and happier world.

DISCLAIMER

———◆◇◆———

This book does not serve as a replacement for medical advice from a licensed medical or health professional. It is intended to be a guide to greater understanding of the hidden energies of the world and the assistance they can provide in understanding our health and wellness. We do not want anyone to think we are attempting to diagnose any disease or condition. Neither the authors nor the publisher accepts any responsibility for your health or how you choose to us this book. The responsibility for using the information in this book is ultimately with you and the members of your health and wellness team. Please note that medical intuitives are not necessarily medical doctors. Not all of those who use muscle testing are licensed practitioners. If you have a health condition, please consult your primary care physician.

The information presented in this book is for educational purposes only. It is intended to help you understand muscle testing and medical intuition, and how they can be utilized together. They may help in the evaluation of wellbeing and health, but are not intended to replace standard medical diagnosis, treatment and monitoring of disease. We do not suggest that you stop taking medications or treatment without first consulting your medical doctor or healthcare provider.

The book is a combination of my practical experience as a working professional medical intuitive for 30 years, and insights provided to Dr. Pat Dougherty DC and myself by professional members of the health and wellness community. Our collaboration has provided me a deeper understanding of my work as a Medical Intuition Teacher/Trainer. I love what I do with medical intuition. There is a great excitement attached to sharing this information with the world. I know we are on the brink of great change in the world view of health care, and I will be part of that. May the information in this book help spark the dialogue needed for change.

Charles Lightwalker Lasol

FOREWORD BY CHARLES LIGHTWALKER

There are three entities in the health care game. Those are the recipient of care, the healthcare provider, and the framework of the healthcare system. Recipients of health care develop a reliance on that which they have been exposed. Often that is the world of drugs and surgery, a self- limited world. It is a world that limits the power of the care recipient.

Knowledge can change that. People exposed to new tools or skills for health and wellness assessment can cast off the limits of the allopathic drugs and surgery world. This book is written for everyone who is ready to explore broader options, especially those who are struggling with health concerns. Frustration with wellness limiting conditions and a lack of help deserves new tools and skills.

For over 40 years, I have observed clients desperate for answers present to me after they had tried "all sorts of treatments". Often, they were advised by allopathic doctors, but with little or no results. Often, I was their last resort. They needed someone to tell them why they were "ill" and not getting better. I used Medical Intuition to supply them with answers and show them a new and different path. The success they found has inspired me to be a part of this book. The world of health and wellness is ready for an expansion, and I can help with that. This book can help with that.

FOREWORD BY PAT DOUGHERTY DC

T here are many facets to this book. Please do not feel it needs to be read from cover to cover. Some chapters may be more challenging than others. That is the nature of melding science and metaphysics. You are welcome to look at the Table of Contents and pick a chapter that looks interesting. Each chapter is written to make sense on its own.

The section of Medical Intuition is the part Charles Lightwalker Lasol contributed. I have taken his rough rendering and hopefully improved it. I needed his perspective for that section and gladly undertook the editing in order to get that perspective. Thank you Charles.

Our work is not, and is not pretending to be, a scientific work. There are more than enough brilliant people in this world who produce incredible insights and discoveries in the scientific field. We are observers and compilers. We observe the work of others and attempt to digest it. We are observers of the universe around us, including the part that is, historically in western culture, considered hidden from view. At times things align in a manner that expands us. Then, the more we observe, the more we become aware of the potential to observe even more.

In this way we began to compile observations of the scientists who have sought to explain the unseen world, and of those who use that unseen energy. The information we collected often served to open new doors of perception for us. The subject we had chosen to explore regularly became larger, exploding into layers of complexity. We were enabled to open more and more avenues of explaining the unseen world that enables medical intuition and muscle testing. An interesting facet is that the layers exposed ever-increasing levels of inclusiveness. The more we observe the more we realize there is no such thing as separateness in our universe. Everything is in some way connected to medical intuition and muscle testing.

As the realizations of this unfolding process evolved, we realized we needed to talk about other disciplines, research and theories. We embraced this realization. One of our goals is to illustrate connectivity at the expense of separateness. Hopefully, our exploration will help people to realize we are part of the same all-inclusive thing that allows for medical intuition and muscle testing.

In his free subscription email, called TUT (Thoughts from the Universe), Mike Dooley emphasizes that there was a time before space where "Divine Intelligence" (his words) was all that existed. That means that all that came later is also Divine Intelligence. If all things are composed of Divine Intelligence, then of what material are you composed? The answer is divine intelligence and all its potential, both within and without you. That potential and intelligence is how and why Medical Intuition and Muscle testing work.

PART ONE:

MUSCLE TESTING

A. How It Works

CHAPTER 1

BIOFEEDBACK SYSTEM OF THE HUMAN BODY

———◆◇◆———

Biofeedback is a mind-body technique that measures electric energy in physiological functions of a body. It can use energetic frequencies introduced through nervous system receptors to enhance control of involuntary body systems and functions. The result may be the ability to gain some voluntary control over parasympathetic functions which are normally involuntary functions. These may include pain perception, heart rate and blood flow and pressure, digestion, and muscle tension.

Biofeedback is able to detect physiological states in the body with electrical sensors. It may use electromyography (EMG) to measure muscle tension and its changes, thermal biofeedback measures body temperature changes, and another type of biofeedback measures brain wave activity. Once aberrant energetic frequencies are detected, then, biofeedback is sometimes used to change those frequencies into something more desirable. Change of frequency can allow stress to be reduced allowing anxiety to be reduced.

This happens due to the electrical nature of a body. Electricity is everywhere including in our bodies and on our bodies. Every cell conducts electrical currents. Scientists have known for a long time that cell activity generates electrical fields that can be measured and detected on the surface of the skin. Physics laws tell us that every electrical current generates a corresponding magnetic field in the surrounding space. Cells are everywhere and that means electrical currents are everywhere. That means the magnetic fields being generated are everywhere and overlapping. Another way of putting that is physics shows us we are all connected, everything is connected.

The nervous system uses electrical currents generated in the cells to send signals to every part of the body. Receptors in the body return messages to the brain. Every thought, emotion, feeling, movement is an electrical event, a vibration, a waveform. We are negatively charged on the inside. The world we inhabit is more positively charged. Differences between the charge on the inside of a cell and the outside of a cell cause an energy exchange. That energy exchange creates more vibrations and waveforms. The waveforms and the magnetic fields they generate exist as part of whatever we choose to label the bigger thing.

The bigger thing is the composite of every energy in existence, past, present and future. That totality of energy has been called many things.. It is a universal life force That I have heard named Cosmic Matrix, Spirit, Universal Intelligence, Grand Organizing Design, ... For the purposes of this book I will refer to it as the Cosmic Matrix. It is helpful to acknowledge the interactions of sound, thought, light, heat, and other energies as integral and equal parts of the Cosmic Matrix. All of those energies, and all substances, have a resonance that is the generation of harmonic vibrations manifesting as waveforms. Every waveform interacts with every waveform it encounters. New waveforms are created. It is an infinite pattern of creation that exists within and without us. From the smallest subatomic particles to immense galaxies beyond our view, everything has a waveform vibrating at a particular resonance. And, they all attract and create other waveforms.

The Cosmic Matrix is a waveform, but it is a waveform that can be seen as a composite of infinite waveforms. The Cosmic Matrix is all possibilities. It is analogous to the environment of the earth. For instance, a stream can flow around impediments like boulders and fallen trees. It can even be diverted far from its initial course. It can be dammed completely or killed with chemicals that transform the water of the stream from life giving to life taking. This demonstrates that while waveforms shape shift, the Cosmic Matrix remains. It is a vessel of endless adaptations. As physics tells us, energy cannot be destroyed, it is always conserved. Acknowledgment of this fact puts us in a tricky situation. It is easy for humans to absolve themselves of responsibility for their actions with a self-ingrained belief that everything is part of a bigger picture. While the bigger picture part is true, we also need to aware that there is a difference between the flow of universal intelligence within the Cosmic Matrix and adaptations caused by human's reckless decisions and behaviors. Because there is a Cosmic Matrix, a higher power, it allows for growth, change and adaptations as healing waveforms.

This subtle differentiation of diverse energies within and a part of the Cosmic Matrix, can help us to keep from simplifying the complexities of the human biofeedback system. As we realize that there is a universal flow, and that we constantly create new waveforms we can use that knowledge to help us maximize the benefits of the human biofeedback system. The Cosmic Matrix is the stream we are born into and then carries us through life. Our actions are adaptive waveforms that can either flow with the stream, or create obstructions within the stream. The stream is the innate intelligence of the Cosmic Matrix. The stream is also a metaphor for our health, the health of the biofeedback system of the human body. We choose our adaptations. That is the basis of epigenetics. The adaptations we choose determine the frequency at which we resonate. That frequency determines the degree of health and wellness we maintain.

We maximize the potential of our biofeedback system when we recognize that distinct energies can provide us distinct advantages when it comes to the utilization of those energies. Those advantages increase in potential when we recognize that the additive effect of multiple energies can exist on a scale that transcends simple addition. It is likely that compounding energies create an effect that multiplies rather than adding. Our choices become our state of health and wellness. The more we ride the waveforms of the Cosmic Matrix, the healthier we become. The more we resist, the more susceptible to ill health we become.

As a species we get to choose from where and how we receive our data. We can tune directly into the Cosmic Matrix as it shapes our Living Matrix. Our subconscious is a combination formulation of data formed from our life experience in conjunction with universal intelligence. We can choose to filter

Biofeedback System of The Human Body

our reality through nothing but our conscious experiences with the external world. The richest source of data is the world that exists outside of us. That world offers data from experiences such as the foods we eat, our physical activities, even our thoughts. The data from those choices are frequencies that interact with our internal frequencies that interact with the frequencies of the Cosmic Matrix. We are creating our world with our choices.

Possibly the most exciting data source is the energy that exists in forms that are not always readily recognized in the Western world. The ancient healing practice of India, Ayurveda, recognizes what are often called the "subtle energies". Ayurveda explains energy in the Vedic texts called the Akashic Records. According to those texts, before the big bang there was already an energetic field known as the Akashic Fields. They existed from the beginning of time. They were the structure of our universe whose nature was space, ether. That nature was described in great detail as vibrational. Space was said to contain infinite energy. This integrated state of vibration is defined as the source for all possible energy and vibrations evolving from the source. In Vedic science matter does not vibrate. The energy of space vibrates creating a force that brings and holds atoms together to form matter. In this way elements are created in sequence from subtle to dense where Akash/space/ether allows for Prana/cosmic energy to be present in all things. That presence is universal intelligence, the Cosmic Matrix.

These are energies that are possibly not even visible or testable. Those energies may eventually be proved to be just as important, if not more important, than the energies western medicine has learned to observe and measure when it comes to human health and wellness. Medical intuitives tap into those energies. Muscle testing is another way of tapping those energies.

Medical Intuition and Muscle Testing:

CHAPTER 2

CELLULAR MATRIX AND THE LIVING MATRIX

In biology, the Extra Cellular Matrix is a three-dimensional network of extracellular macromolecules, such as collagen, enzymes, and glycoproteins, that provide structural and biochemical support to surrounding cells. The Extra Cellular Matrix is the non-cellular component present within all tissues and organs, and provides not only essential physical scaffolding for the cellular constituents but also initiates crucial biochemical and biomechanical cues that are required for tissue cell growth and differentiation.

The Extra Cellular Matrix needs to remain healthy in order to perform its duties of tissue growth and electrical conduction. Unfortunately it is susceptible to numerous injurious insults. All of the following are common human conditions that injure the extra cellular Matrix and diminish its ability to perform its functions:

- Toxicity

- Physical injury

-   **Poor nutrition**

-   **Chronic inflammation**

-   **Dehydration**

Drugs and surgery offer little to repair and enhance the health of the Extra Cellular Matrix.

The term Living Matrix goes back to the 19th century when Claude Bernard, a French physiologist coined the term to describe the interior environment of the body. In the 1940's and onward Albert Szent-Gyorgyi conducted research that led to widespread acceptance of the idea that semiconductor properties exist in all parts of the Extra Cellular Matrix. Those properties allow the Living Matrix to function as a supremely complex computer processor. The transmission of energy occurs between molecules of the Extra Cellular Matrix via electro magnetic fields. As many as 99% of the body's molecules are water and they comprise two thirds, or more, of the body's volume. The properties of water create an inner electrical environment for communication. That environment can be influenced by many, if not all, forms of energy. That means light, sound, thoughts and more can be used to elicit responses within the body. Those responses can be used by Medical Intuition and muscle testing practitioners. They responses can be used for information gathering, and for transformative healing.

The Living Matrix is a dynamic space within us that is continuous with the Cosmic Matrix. The link between the two is the plasma of the Extra Cellular Matrix. The inside of every cell in our body is interacting with its surrounding cytoplasm, the Extra Cellular Matrix. Integrins are receptors that transmit the electrical charge/information back and forth across cell membranes to the Extra Cellular Matrix. The result is a mechanical and energetic link to all of a person's connective tissue. Connective tissue is substances in the body that enable us to maintain the shape of the body and the form of organs and glands. It provides internal binding and support. Due to the electrical nature of the Extra Cellular Matrix substances, messaging is transmitted throughout the body via connective tissues of the Extra Cellular Matrix. Transmissions reach the Living Matrix, the only organ that touches every cell in the body. Information in any area of the Living Matrix has been shared with all other areas of the matrix. The brain processes all of this activity. We are afforded the opportunity to put it in the contest of the vibrations of the Cosmic Matrix.

All of the communication between the matrices happens at lightning-fast speeds. James Oschman PhD is the president of Nature's Own Research Association that is exploring the scientific basis for complementary and alternative medicines. He has built on Szent-Gyorgyi's research. His work shows that the transmission properties of the Living Matrix are similar to, and much of the time, faster than the network of nerves in the body known as the nervous system.

It appears that the meridian channels of Oriental Medicine/acupuncture are the primary channels for Living Matrix high speed communication. The hydrated crystalline network in its highly electrified state allows piezoelectric (electric charge in response to applied mechanical stress), pyroelectric (generate an electrical potential when they are heated or cooled) and thermoelectric (create a voltage when there is a different temperature on each side) transmissions. While all cells in the Extra Cellular Matrix are connected, it is the specialized networks of cells in the meridians that allow organ and gland specific communications that are so valuable in healing arts. That these networks are faster than the cells of the nervous system affords them greater communication efficiency.

Our skin is the second largest organ in the body, after the Living Matrix. Because the skin is part of the Living Matrix it uses thermoelectric effects to conduct energy and information beyond itself. This is inevitable as the Integrins travel back and forth across cell membranes. Therein lies the direct link for the Living Matrix communication with what Oschman called the Cosmic Matrix. The Cosmic Matrix is a living intelligent universe. It gets its electrons, the source of its electrical transmission, from suns, lightning, thunder and other natural events. Every biochemical reaction in the body is a redox reaction. This means every reaction requires electron transfers to complete a task. Our internal Living Matrix redox reactions are smaller versions of the sun and all it touches with its light.

This means the Living Matrix is constantly accessing the energy, thus information, contained in the Cosmic Matrix. Every living body is a part of the Cosmic Matrix and all its universal intelligence. Traditional western analytical paradigms use vague language to represent what analytical reasoning may not understand. The result is terms like universal mind/intelligence/consciousness, Spirit, God, Cosmic Matrix are poorly defined and understood. Modern science though gives us a link to understand those terms from an energetic, verifiable viewpoint. They all are electrical conduction systems of energy passing messages back and forth. Everything, seen and unseen, is an electrical conductor information within the Cosmic Matrix. Metaphysical practices from the Far East have long incorporated models of consciousness into this formula. We are currently seeing the effects of quantum mechanics pushing western metaphysics toward an awareness of the effect of the observer on consciousness. It is the communication within the Cosmic, Living and Extracellular matrices that is the observer.

Because all the cells in the body transmit information, humans act as a magnificent supercomputer capable of infinite communication. One of the most effective communication modes in the body is the spine. The spine exists as a subset of the Living Matrix, much as the meridians act as a subset also. Both the spine and meridians have different electrical properties than surrounding tissues.

The spine has receptors in multiple areas that transmit signals to the spinal cord on up to the cerebellum in the brain. From the cerebellum transmissions are passed along to higher centers in the cortex of the brain. From there messaging is transmitted back down to the spine. Those communications enable function of not only the muscles and joints of the skeleton, but also to organs, glands and even smaller structures. Of course, clearer communication allows for more optimal function in the body.

The above mode of communication is dependent on motion in the spine. The more optimally the spine moves, then the more optimally the body functions due to proper clarity and timing of communication. All of this happens not due to human volition, but rather because of the innate knowledge inherent in the Living Matrix. That innate knowledge is the link between the Living Matrix and the Cosmic Matrix. Ultimately it is a person's relationship to the Cosmic Matrix that enables Living Matrix to feed our innate intelligence. The expression of that intelligence is the infinite possibility of all facets of life. The more we can do on the physical, chemical and emotional planes of wellness to enhance our vibration, the more innate intelligence we express and the closer we are to Medical Intuition.

There is a therapy named earthing. Earthing uses the body's electrical conduction properties to enhance the energy in the body. The theory is that when our body has contact with earth that retains at least some measure of moisture, then it will gather electrons from the earth that will stimulate our cells. The stimulation will contribute to optimizing cellular function in the body. Many believe this is due to what acupuncture calls the kidney meridian. The first point in the kidney meridian is on the heel on each side of the body. When we are barefoot on the earth the kidney meridian circulates energy via its pathway throughout the body.

It is no accident that any of the above communication can happen with earthing. Electrons are the generators of bodily chemical reactions. Oxidation-reduction (redox) reactions are transfers of electrons between two species, typically a molecule or atom. These take place in body cells and are involved in the production of the body's energy source, ATP. Redox reactions release energy.

Earthing has been shown to use redox reactions, in as little as 15 minutes a day, to enhance sleep and relaxation. Earthing appears to enhance the autonomic nervous system, the part of the nervous system responsible for control of the bodily functions not consciously directed. This includes breathing, heart, senses, and digestive functions, even some thoughts. These processes can promote healing by enhancing Heart Rate Variability (HRV). Science has provided us methods for measuring HRV.

HRV is the physiological fact that the heartbeat of a human is not a constant consistent pattern. The constant variable interval between heartbeats is the link between the automatic functions of our body, and the voluntarily controlled functions of the body. High HRV means a person is in a more relaxed state that allows better function of processes that decrease inflammation and pain. This in turn promotes healing by controlling the modulation of cortisol and blood viscosity. This innate function of the body allows automatic adjustments in our physiology in order to allow us to respond seamlessly to the demands of the external world. The inside joke is that our innate internal state is a part of the extrinsic world. We are responding to our self, and the less friction

16

created in that response the healthier we will be. That enhanced degree of health results in enhanced degree of clarity. Greater clarity equates to more effective medical intuition, and/or muscle testing.

The Living Matrix provides insight into energy in general and energy flow in the human body. Ever increasing amounts of scientific research documents illustrate these energy fields. We have evidence of how those fields are generated. It has also been illustrated and documented how energy fields are altered by disease, emotions and injury.

We live in a time when holistic healing methods are being applied more frequently to restore healthy flow of energy in the body. A driving force in this trend is the recognition that conventional medicine has failed mightily in addressing many of the conditions that afflict modern society. Medical intuition and muscle testing can be accurate and effective mechanisms for the evaluation of mind and body processes, and for the selection of methods to address faulty processes.

It makes sense that when we utilize energetic methods of analysis we would also use energetic healing methods to address the body's healing and performance potential. This has led to an explosion of holistic and spiritual health and wellness modes in the western world. These modes utilize waveforms, frequencies, vibration and tone for the repair and regeneration of health and wellness. The unseen world is colliding with, and melding with the medical world via discoveries in biology and physics. The abstract is melding with the practical. The results are deeper understanding of dis-ease, healing, life and beyond. Separateness is becoming inclusiveness. Medical intuition and muscle testing are integral parts at the forefront of this movement.

CHAPTER 3:

MOLECULES OF EMOTION

————◆◇◆————

Energetic molecules and waveforms in the body impact humans in many ways. One area they can influence is emotions. A pioneer in this field is Candace Pert. Her classic 1997 book, <u>The Molecules of Emotion</u>, brought the electrical nature of emotions to the general public's attention. It was customary at that time to think of emotions as an esoteric concept without physical substance. Her book, bolstered by her part in the 2004 movie, What the Bleep Do We Know!?, laid a foundation for an expanded understanding of emotions. Her work examined emotions from a physiological and electrical perspective that presented them as scientifically observable event.

The word emotion is derived from the Latin root, emotere, which means energy in motion. In spite of the definition of emotere, emotion was historically seen as energetically neutral. The physiological reaction associated with emotion was feeling. We realize now that there has to be a. That transition was acknowledged to be a carrier wave. The word wave brings us back to the crux of the matter. Everything is energy, waveforms. It is nonsensical to acknowledge emotion is a carrier wave yet not acknowledge its energetic measurable existence. The transition between emotion and feelings is our vibratory electrical nature. We broadcast and receive by virtue of our vibrations. Those vibrations transform emotion to feeling.

Our body is an electrical neural broadcasting system. When we strive to expand that system, the resulting emotions create new neural connections. Emotions broadcast from the field of all information, the Cosmic Matrix. Emotions literally wire a pathway that can enhance access to the Cosmic Matrix. The greater our access to that matrix the more conscious we can become in the present moment. Then, we begin to see the infinite possibilities of the eternal quantum field that is the Cosmic Matrix.

Neurotransmitters are the vehicle for the transition vibrations from emotion to feelings. Neurotransmitters are measurable peptides that carry emotional messages. Like everything else, neuropeptides are electrical matter, a vibratory signal. Feelings are the resultant chemical change in the body's cells. Emotions become a scientifically observable event as we measure the electrical charge. Neuropeptide vibration is the passage of waves between the brain and the body. The result manifests as feeling which can also be measured. Every cell in the body is a receptor site for these electrochemical messages.

Like every other process in our lives, emotions can be viewed on a micro level, or on a macro level. The micro level is that neuropeptides that trigger emotions change a body chemically and electrically. The macro level is the infinity of the divinity of the Living Matrix within the Cosmic Matrix. The emotionally electrified body is also exchanging vibrations with the cells outside of the body. Any exchange of vibrational energy forms a new vibration. Emotions change us and our energetic appearance. Those changes are part of what the medical Intuitive and the muscle tester pick up on. The changes meld seamlessly into the Cosmic Matrix.

To flow with the stream of innate knowledge provided by the Cosmic Matrix is to create an inner emotional resonance. When we create emotions that block the stream we deteriorate emotionally, physically, chemically and electrically. The brain waves of emotions are not confined to the brain. The Extracellular Matrix is the medium that conveys emotional messages through our Living Matrix. As the molecules of emotion course through the body they appear to amplify courtesy of the electrical properties of the Extra Cellular Matrix. We can use that amplification to enhance the conscious creative mind, but also to overcome the negative emotions of habitual subconscious tape loops. Intentional creation of emotions can help to create the life we want. It can help eliminate subconscious debilitating tape loops. That is a decision to follow divine knowledge of the Cosmic Matrix. It is a decision that starts with the molecules of emotion and ends with new neural connections.

The long held beliefs of scientists that unseen energies do not exist in the body are currently being eroded due to the efforts of innovative and curious scientists. Once taken for granted that no energy field exists around the human body there is scarcely anyone left in scientific fields who will contest their existence today. It is a certainty that we are an energy field. Research is prevalent in the role of those fields in disease and wellness. There no longer is any basis for a disbelief in energy healing. Moreover it is now readily acknowledged that brain waves spread throughout the body from Extra Cellular Matrix to Living Matrix to Cosmic Matrix. The language may vary but the acknowledgment of energy fields within and without the human body has been firmly established.

Robert Becker, author of The Body Electric, published at the turn of the last century; described how the body's electrical system is the primary system for injury regulation and repair processes in the body. As healing methods evolve there will be more and more demand for healers who can read and interpret the body's energy patterns.

For centuries sensitive individuals have been reading the body's energy. Western medicine, though, had no way to measure the energy that was being read. Now there are instruments capable of detecting miniscule energy fields surrounding and in the body. They see what is unseen to the naked eye. This has helped immensely with the acceptance of energy medicine interventions. One such instrument is the SQUID magnetometer. SQUID is an acronym for Superconducting Quantum Interference Device. Scientists discovered that SQUID could detect bio magnetic fields that show energy changes as the body's physiology changes. Initially it was used to measure bio magnetic fields produced by the heart then the brain. Eventually, it was discovered that all organs and glands produced specific bio magnetic fields that the SQUID could measure. The tiny magnetic fields show up some distance from the body. Currently scientists believe that the magnetic fields surrounding the body often are more accurate indicators of physiology, maybe even pathology, than traditional electrical measurements of hearts, brains, and other organs and glands. SQUID technology has even been used to demonstrate the pulsed biomagnetic fields that emanate from the hands of some healers.

From this modern understanding of the body as an electrical biofeedback machine came the realization that the Extra Cellular Matrix and its extra body projections could predict physical symptoms and diseases before they happened. The next step is to prevent the symptoms and diseases before they happen. Light, sound waves and other energy techniques now tap into this possibility. Research goes on around the world confirming these ideas. The interesting factor for this book is that machines are now doing what energetically sensitive healers have done for centuries.

Instruments are being used to map the ways disease alters the energy fields surrounding the body. One of the most interesting SQUID findings was when the instrument measured a huge energetic field coming out of the hands of a therapist at work. The field pulsed through a frequency range that corresponded to brain wave frequencies. Studies showed that these frequency sweeps were traveling through a full range of known healing frequencies. What had been the mystery of misunderstood healers and their techniques had become undeniable to the scientific community.

These findings were later confirmed when researchers in Japan studied martial arts practitioners. They found that a magnetometer, a wire coil instrument used for measuring magnetic forces, easily detected the energy "Qi" emitted from the hands of practitioners. This was followed by numerous studies measuring the sound, light and thermal fields emitted by Qigong practitioners, then other Reiki practitioners and other healers.

Building on the frequency work of Royal Rife in the 1930's devices such as lasers, other light and sound devices are prevalent in the holistic healing fields today. We are much closer to reconciling spiritual and metaphysical mysteries of life with the science of the allopathic medical field. As the gap between the two shrinks we are closer to acknowledging the verifiable existence and impact of the Molecules of Emotion. We also are closing in on widespread acceptance of the use of Medical Intuition and muscle testing as valuable tools in a world in need of healing and regeneration.

CHAPTER 4:

BRAIN ACTIVITY

———◆◇◆———

Medical intuition and muscle testing are greatly affected by how we use our brains. In general, it is believed that if a person is left brain dominant, then their thinking will be methodical and analytical. Right brain dominant people are believed to be more creative. Though this is somewhat true, it is also true that humans are both left and right brained. A strip called the corpus callosum connects the two sides of the brain, known as the left and right cortex. In reality both cortices are involved in most if not all processes. Additionally, many humans are creative and analytical at the same time.

Some scientists make the argument that the creative side of the brain is more imaginative, psychic, intuitive, even childlike. This is probably true. Watching children at play supports that theory. Of course, there are varying degrees of the intuitive creative nature in children. This is one of the many characteristics that scientists thought they would be able to explain with the science of genetics.

Ever since the Human Genome Project (HGP) was completed and fully published in 2003 it has been acknowledged, that in many ways, humans are not as complex as many scientists previously believed. The total numbers of genes discovered were less than a quarter of what was expected, and that number is expected to drop in the future as research continues. Some thought that the HGP would give the medical field all the information they needed to cure any disease or condition. This turned out to be patently false.

The observable fact that children appear to be more creative and intuitive as a whole than adults lends some understanding to the findings of the HGP. After the failure to define humans precisely with genetics, the study of our genes, a new field arose; epigenetics. Epigenetics is derived from Greek roots and literally means above genetics. This means that scientists had to move beyond their genetic theories. The result was a new field that studied the impact of human lifestyles on the expression of their genetics.

If we examine children in the context of epigenetics we can start to explain why they are often more creative and intuitive than adults. Most cultures promote the development of intellect and the stability and security that shared values and knowledge apparently produce. Consequently, social norms often funnel children into predictable patterns of thought and behavior. Growing up in a society that neither accepts, or encourages, qualities of intuition, ESP and psychic abilities; it is natural that the creative intuition of child hood diminishes as we grow up. This is certainly true for the majority of children in the United States.

Because we are all part of the Cosmic Matrix with access to all of the knowledge therein, intuition is a natural state. It can be a part of our genetic state. But that genetic state is either turned on and enhanced or discouraged and shut off by life experiences. That is epigenetics. Epigenetics is a light switch that leads us into darkness, or light – or somewhere in between.

Intuition, like Medical Intuition and muscle testing, is a matter of to what degree we access the Cosmic Matrix and make it a part of our Living Matrix. In other words, we all have the same ability to access intuition and put it to use in our everyday life. Once we acknowledge this we can begin to examine what activities enhance, and what activities detract from intuition. That is the epigenetic connection. Children generally have less social conditioning and are more likely to play in the intuitive field.

When social conditioning has molded adult activities in a way that suppresses intuition, then regaining the ability may take some extreme efforts.

Though the effort may have to be extreme, the activity itself does not necessarily need to be extreme. There are many examples of some of history's brightest minds escaping from the busy intellectual thought patterns in order to tap the more intuitive part of their being without intense effort.

Albert Einstein reportedly sat in his rocking chair gazing at the clouds. He would become very dizzy and fall into a hypnotic trance. While in the trance-like state he asked questions and answers came to him.

Thomas Edison reportedly would sit in a chair with ball bearings in his hands. He would squeeze as hard as he could for as long as possible. After about five minutes the ball bearings would fall from his exhausted hand. He then asked questions about his future inventions and the answers came to him.

Nikola Tesla reportedly received detailed images in his mind of his many inventions. Sometimes the blueprints in his mind were so vivid and detailed he would forego writing down a physical blueprint.

These examples show that all the knowledge in the universe is already in existence. When the mind quiets the right question can come, soon followed by the answer, Guidance and direction are available for the asking. The key is still the chatter in our minds because that chatter blocks the ability of the universal intelligence to become innate intelligence.

Edgar Cayce called prayer "talking to God" and meditation "listening to God". It is common for people to be better at asking and talking than at listening. The practices of medical intuition and muscle testing are listening abilities, and they take practice. Part of that practice is learning to quiet the busy conscious brain.

The above examples may sound vague and mysterious, but when we explore the science of brain waves the mystery begins to dissolve. Examine the brain wave states below to begin to understand why the examples worked for Einstein, Edison, Tesla, and Cayce:

> A. **Delta (0.5-4Hz):** Delta waves are a deep dreamless sleep and very deep, transcendental meditation/unconscious brain wave in adults. It is also the state in which infants spend much of their first two years of life, including their time in the womb.

24

B. **Theta (4-7.5Hz):** Theta waves are strong during deep meditation, prayer, light sleep, the REM dream state. It is also the adult subconscious mind state. Vivid visualizations, inspiration, profound creativity, exceptional insight are Theta characteristics. In Theta we also are highly programmable as we automatically accept what we see hear and feel. This state occurs regularly from age 2-6 in kids, and is perfectly normal in children up to age 13

C. **Alpha-Theta border (7-8Hz)** is the optimal range for visualization, creativity and mind programming. It is the mental state that is the frequency bridge between the subconscious (Theta) mind and our conscious (Beta) thinking. This is where we consciously create our reality while the body is in deep relaxation. We appear to need fewer reps for change in this frequency zone. This brain wave state is known to calm us and promote feelings of contentment and deep relaxation.

D. **Alpha (7.5-12Hz)** is the state of deep relaxation, with the eyes usually closed, of quietly flowing thoughts. Light meditation, and daydreaming are common here for adults. Successful mind programming is another characteristic of Alpha brain waves. Alpha heightens imagination, visualization, memory, learning and concentration. Intuition is enhanced in this resting brain state that resides in the present. This is where we learn analysis, mental coordination and mind body integration. In an Alpha state it is believed 21 repetitions are needed for change.

E. **Beta (12-30Hz)** brain waves are associated with normal waking consciousness in adults. In Beta we interact cognitively with the world around us. Logic and critical reasoning are used for problem solving, but activity is rapid and that can translate into stress, anxiety and restlessness. Although we can be alert and attentive, the busy nature of Beta means thousands of repetitions are needed for us to affect change. The essence of the Beta state is as close to the antithesis of an intuitive state as humans can attain.

F.   Gamma (30-100Hz): The most recently discovered range is Gamma which is the fastest in frequency at above 40Hz (some researchers do not distinguish Beta from Gamma waves). Initial research shows Gamma waves are associated with bursts of insight and high-level information processing.

Once we have explored the effects of the differing brain waves on our behavior it starts to become clear that children are at an advantage when it comes to tapping into their intuition. Their brain waves are simply more conducive to intuition than the busy Beta waves of adulthood.

An exploration of the course of what happens when we are children takes us back to the discussion on epigenetics. Genetically kids are programmed to spend most of their first six years in delta and theta wave frequencies. That is what makes them so open to intuition, the wave of information from the Cosmic Matrix. But, as noted earlier, genes rarely predispose us to anything. Genes are like a light switch, and it is epigenetic factors that flip that switch on and off.

Epigenetic factors include foods, toxins, physical traumas, and especially in those first six years; what the child is told by authority figures. There can be other epigenetic factors, but the one that has the most relevance to intuition is what the child is told. When we realize that information transfer can happen with each exchange when in a delta or theta state, then we can understand how detrimental it might be to a child to be told to "stop imagining things", or to "get serious". The playful imagination is what keeps a child in touch with their intuition. The more intuition is repressed in a child, the harder it makes it for that person to get back in touch with their intuition. But there is a level of information available to humans past the levels of genetics and epigenetics. That level is the fertile field of intuition allowed to interact freely with the Cosmic Matrix. The child whose intuition is nurtured is at an advantage when they try to tap into the Cosmic Matrix, and into the fields of medical intuition and muscle testing as they grow into adulthood.

The result of the many restrictions placed on children is an adult society that is widely closed off from intuition. Many adults will never begin the work of moving back toward a more intuitive approach to life. Many of those who

26

attempt the move in the direction of redeveloping and utilizing their intuition will find the journey difficult and arduous. Consequently, as things currently stand we live in a society dominated by "science " at the expense of intuition. A further result of a society closed off from intuition is a medical system like we see in the United States, an allopathic system that is dependent on drugs and surgery. In that system the elimination of symptoms takes precedence over the development and maintenance of wellness. To change to a more effective system is going to take a new mindset.

We need to question how we undo the subconscious to create that new mindset. We know that we can create a heightened state awareness by paying attention and cultivating the correct brain waves for change. Consciousness is derived from awareness. Awareness allows us to observe more, both in the seen and in the unseen world. Then we see ourselves and others in a more revealing light. The more we observe the more we reprogram the subconscious programs of womb to six, if necessary. Repetition is the key to undoing previous subconscious programming.

The new mindset will be welcoming, and in need of, medical intuitives. The science of the brain supports this contention. It's happening, don't get left behind.

ᛈART ONE:

Muscle Testing

B. Parameters For Muscle Testing

CHAPTER 5

THE HISTORY OF MUSCLE TESTING

———◆◇◆———

Manual muscle testing is a method of communicating with the body and mind of another person. A structural muscle test is a brief pull or push to a body part of the person being tested by the tester. A body part is chosen that isolates a muscle action. The tester uses thoughts, words or touch to induce energetic shifts in the muscle being tested. This allows the practitioner to assess the muscle's function as the body sets off a neurological and energetic response. How quickly and firmly the muscle responds supplies information to the tester. Today chiropractors, neurologists and medical doctors all use manual muscle testing in neurologic examinations to assess neurological muscle function.

There are some indications that muscle testing was used thousands of years ago health practitioners in China and other far-eastern countries. The first documented use of muscle testing in the western world I could find was at a university in Stockholm, Sweden in the mid to late 1800's. Manual medicine techniques were taught there well before the creation of osteopathy and chiropractic.

Early muscle testers were using structural muscle testing. It was a way to tell whether the nerves that supply a joint, via a muscle connected to that joint, were delivering clear enough data to the muscle to allow it to function properly. From there the tester could assess whether the interference of communication came from the brain, the brain stem, nerve roots in the spine, or damage to the joint where the muscle connected, or even to the muscle itself.

Later, in the 20th century, manual muscle testing became popular as a method of assessing polio victim's deficits. The type of muscle testing written about in this book is vastly different from muscle strength testing. When this book refers to muscle testing, we refer to the using the testing to assess an individual's relationship within their self and without. It is a combination of science and art in the effort to evaluate a person's neuromuscular system. The goal wherein is to optimize a person's health.

A very early transition, in the 1930's, from strength test to communication testing was made by using the muscle to give information about other parts of the body. This was explored by a surgeon named RW Lovett and an osteopath named Frank Chapman. Their interest in lymph flow disruption led to the correlation of touch on certain lymph system points to improvement of associated conditions. Out of their work came the work of a chiropractor, Terence Benner, who devised a system of points associated with conditions. Those points are still used today in multiple kinesiology disciplines (Applied Kinesiology, Clinical Kinesiology, Wholisitc Kinesiology, etc.). They are neurovascular points. The transition into a communication method to assess organs, glands, pathogens, toxins, emotions, nutritive values and more continued, primarily though the investigations of chiropractors. Additionally, two physical therapists, H.O. and F.M.P. Kendall published <u>Muscles-Testing and Function</u>. That 1949 text expanded the concept of using muscle testing to evaluate Nervous system function.

Probably the biggest breakthrough in muscle testing began to happen in 1964 when Dr. George Goodheart, DC. and a team of researchers were studying the function of joints and muscles. When testing the strength of various muscle groups Dr. Goodheart observed specific relationships between muscles, organs and glands. Later he related those findings to the meridian system of Chinese medicine. This led him to develop a technique he named Applied Kinesiology. He found that a blockage in a meridian caused associated muscles to weaken. These observations led to muscle testing being used to assess the totality of the nervous system rather than the strength a muscle produced.

Goodheart was a pioneer in the advancement of muscle testing, but he was not alone. Over the years I have studied with many chiropractors who participated with Goodheart in the development of muscle testing. Among those doctors were Paul White, DC and Wally Schmidt, DC. They were participants in a group of 12 practitioners who met regularly to compare notes and advance the practice of Applied Kinesiology. They were sometimes referred to as the "Dirty Dozen". During seminars I have heard stories about their brainstorming processes in this development. After meeting they would take their latest discoveries and theories back to their offices. Patients were the proving ground for the knowledge they were accumulating. Their consistent sessions led to the Applied Kinesiology becoming an intensely complex system of points and tests that confronted health and wellness in a manner never before conceived. In 1981 David Walther, in conjunction with George Goodheart, published Applied Kinesiology. To this day that book, to the best of my knowledge, continues to be the best and most comprehensive published account of the practice of muscle testing.

Not everyone sought to make muscle testing so complex, however. One of Goodheart's early collaborators, John Thie, DC, sought to make muscle testing accessible to lay people. He developed a system and book called Touch for Health. This simplified version brought many practitioners and lay people into the world of muscle testing. Touch For Health remains a valuable tool for many in the present-day world of health and wellness.

Another version of muscle testing, Clinical Kinesiology, was developed by Alan Beardall, DC. Beardall's method differed from Applied Kinesiology with its attention to a patient's subconscious dialogue. This turned out to be a missing component in some patient's recovery from traumatic events. His system was able to penetrate the Extra Cellular Matrix in order to find stagnant cellular restrictions. These restrictions, at times, would create an adaptive pattern that resisted a normal physical intervention. It also allowed for the release of no longer needed physical compensations that were deeply imbedded in the subconscious mind.

Beardall's Clinical Kinesiology work has led to several techniques that chiropractor's use to diminish the effects of trapped cellular emotions. These include chiropractor Scott Walker's "NET" method, the work of John Brimhall

DC, various tapping techniques, and more. The basis of Clinical Kinesiology tapping into the subconscious has even become an integral part of modern psychology. Examples of this are various tapping techniques, Behavioral Kinesiology, and especially the wildly popular and exploding field of "Eye Movement Desensitization and Reprocessing" (EMDR). Muscle testing development has helped the health world understand the importance of accessing subconscious adaptive patterns from stored cellular memories. This has become especially important in dealing with an explosion of "Post Traumatic Stress Disorder" brought on by our pathologically stressful environment in the world today.

An interesting corollary of the use of muscle testing is the work of David R. Hawkins M.D. Ph.D. in psychology. His expanded the research showed us that muscle testing can be used to distinguish between truth and falsehood. His work utilized the fact that the body's computer has access to knowledge beyond the conscious level of a brain.

Applied Kinesiology muscle testing and many of its derivatives provide access to the body's internal computer. Because the body is connected to the Cosmic Matrix this internal computer has unlimited knowledge. The Cosmic Matrix knows much more than the limited ego is aware of. It is part of the cosmic computer is not limited by the conscious knowledge of the thinking brain. The body's computer regulates millions of functions. Many of which we are unaware. Many of these functions happen outside of our volition, and sometimes outside of our awareness. This includes some of a body's most important functions. These include heart functions, breathing digestion, immune system activity and much more.

Because the body's computer knows much more than our conscious mind it is a valuable source of information for the muscle tester. The body's computer can inform the tester of things that are good for us and things that are harmful to us.

A lot of different styles of muscle testing have evolved over the years. The standard for muscle testing is using the resistance of a body part. But, there are other styles that have come to be classified as muscle testing. Many testers use a pendulum to get answers. They hold the pendulum stationary and watch to see

Medical Intuition and Muscle Testing:

whether it begins to swing clockwise, or counter clockwise. One direction will be a positive answer and the other a negative answer.

Self-testing has become a big part of the muscle testing field. Self-testing is when a person asks a question of their own self. The same methods used can also be used when asking questions about another person. The most common methods I have seen are styles using finger friction, nail friction, or finger strength. The same parameters exist for self-testing as for the communication testing used when testing another person. Confidence and clarity on the part of the tester are absolutely necessary no matter what method of muscle testing is used.

Medical Intuition and Muscle Testing:

CHAPTER 6

INTUITIVE MINDSET

Humans are a member of an ecosystem, and humans are an ecosystem. Both ecosystems are composed of light energy. We are light energy. Life is a transformative experience. The ultimate transformative experience is to realize we are not simply a being of physiology, biology and chemistry; but rather a spiritual being of light energy. The physical body is the vehicle for the transformative journey.

The journey is largely regulated by chemical signals produced in the brain. Some are conducive to an intuitive mindset, some not. The limbic system is the set of structures in the brain that regulates whether we remain rational, or become irrational in the presence of stress. In reality it is our reaction to stress, not stress itself that determines whether stress allows us to grow, or be diminished.

The limbic system has several parts, including the thalamus, amygdala, hippocampus, hypothalamus, basal ganglia, cingulate gyrus. The limbic system deals with emotions and memory. It controls much of the regulation of autonomic parasympathetic system (the system of non-thinking reactions like breathing, digestion and the heart) and the endocrine system (the body's chemical messenger system).

In simplified terms, sensory organs (taste, smell, hearing and more) send information to the limbic system. The hippocampus is stored memory of everything a person has ever experienced. It is the part of the limbic system that stores rational responses to experiences. The amygdala is the emotional irrational part of the limbic system. When the amygdala finds a match in the hippocampus that has previously been perceived as a threat it signals the brain's pituitary gland which signals the adrenal glands. Adrenal glands, perceiving a threat, release fight or flight hormones. Hormones are chemical messengers. Fight or flight hormones shunt blood to the extremities.

This leaves a lack of blood for the parasympathetic viscera, and the brain. Things get blown out of proportion and we act irrationally. The result, under the influence of mishandled stress we become more stupid. There is no energy to utilize for growth and maintenance. Intuition is buried.

Stress induced fight or flight reactions shut down the immune system. We all have numerous pathogens in and on us that are controlled by the immune system. This is the beginning of dis-ease. Dis-ease shuts down life. Poor reactions to stress shut down intuition and wellness oriented automatic reactions. Wellness is not just the absence of stress, though. We have the amazing capacity to replace countless cells daily. That is how we grow and stay healthy. The more we grow every day, the more we maintain wellness and experience increased love and joy. That is how health and our intuition expand.

As stated in the first paragraph, life is a transformative experience. The best transformations happen via the love emotion. The more our actions and thoughts are directed by love, the closer we get to the realization we are a spiritual being. Fear, anger and other negative emotions are the physical body speaking to us and holding us back from love and transformation. There is a beauty in everything, and all things are a reflection of and a clue to our inner selves. When we choose to see the beauty in all things, we choose to see love created and manifested. There is a beauty, even in things that hurt, and to see that beauty is a major step in manifesting our light energy as a spiritual being.

Every day we are faced with choices. As I write this our ability to transform is being challenged by fear of Covid and death, and by anxiety over having to come to terms with the notion of Anglo-Saxon protestant superiority that has fueled our nation since its inception. Fear changes our physiology. But so do our positive experiences. Experience is the universe talking to us and allowing a changed reaction to the external world. Change allows creation of new genomic information.

Experience guided by physical, chemical and emotional stress can cause a fearful reaction. It can overwhelm the ability to see the beauty of life and react with love. Then our health and our genetic makeup are diminished. We have, as a nation, moved toward increasing stressful toxicity since entering the 20th century. Agriculture toxicity, pollutants, pharmaceutical dependence, endless wars, and fear have slowly infiltrated the culture of this country. Currently between 40 and 50% of all the people in the U.S. have preventable chronic lifestyle disease(s). Lifestyle diseases are a physiological change that makes us more susceptible to Covid and other disease. They are also a barrier between an individual and their transformative spiritual experience.

Fortunately none of that is our destiny. We can visualize life as creative fulfillment, friends and lovers, financial and physical security, dancing and singing and helping others. This speeds our transformative spiritual experience. Intuition is both the link to and the result of the transformative spiritual experience.

Holistic healers can look at an individual with medical intuition, muscle testing, and other methods. Those methods allow them to find the stresses that are counterproductive to physical and spiritual growth. Then solutions become apparent. Growth is then possible. This is important because simultaneous growth and the fear induced by fight or flight reactions are impossible. To pursue the transformative spiritual experience, it is necessary to see stress as the opportunity for growth and the development of intuition.

We must learn to choose. Choose to not break down. Choose to break through to where we are being woven together. When we raise our awareness of the fact we are not separate we enter the Living Matrix, the pathway to the Cosmic Matrix. No longer separate we become Universal Intelligence. Our intuition simply becomes natural in that state of being. Then Medical Intuition and muscle testing are readily available to us.

39

CHAPTER 7

CONFIDENCE AND CLARITY

Muscle testing is an art. Anybody can do it. The trick is to use it in a manner that produces accurate and reproducible results. Some people lapse into a good muscle testing mental state easily, maybe naturally. For many though the path to accurate muscle testing is arduous.

When muscle testing is arduous I believe it is due to two factors initially. Those factors are confidence and clarity. Once confidence and clarity are mastered and muscle testing becomes an accurate way of assessing things, then the fun really begins. That fun is the utilization of double and triple negatives that allow a practitioner to probe ever deeper levels of examination and solutions to the energetic imbalances that are revealed.

On the way to becoming confident and clear there are several things to keep in mind. It is possible for the tester to introduce too many variables into an equation. A muscle responds instantaneously to variable factors. These can be inadvertently introduced by the tester. An example would be for the tester to be thinking of a thing that has nothing to do with the test. If you are thinking of where you will go to lunch an extra energetic frequency is entered into the equation. Begin to think of your spouse when you should be having an exclusive interaction with the person you are testing and you will create confusion. It is like trying to make 2+2 = 4 when you have introduced an extra number; 2+2+2 will never = 4. The attention needs to be focused on nothing but the questions you ask.

Energy will always follow intention when you are muscle testing. Conscious intention is the part of intention we most have control over when we muscle test. The conscious intent needs to be to pose a question and then have the conscious mind get out of the way. Neutrality is encouraged when the conscious mind recedes into the background. A bias can easily be introduced if the tester has a feeling as to what the answer should be. The tester's energy will affect the testee's energetic response. Neutrality is a lack of preconceived notions about muscle responses. That letting go allows us to remain neutral. Although conscious intention is emphasized here, it is also important to realize that subconscious preconceived notions are just as harmful to the muscle testing process. It is up to a tester to do the work they need to do in order to remain an empty vessel when they test. My best suggestion for doing this is to willfully establish a connection to the Cosmic Matrix and hold that connection when you test.

Sometimes the tester lacks a clarity as to what is a positive answer, and what is a negative answer. Though this sounds like a simple thing, I have been at seminars where practice sessions turned into a chaotic scene that filled a room. This was often due to the people learning to test losing track of what they were looking for and when. The result of that was often forgetting the simplest of things – like 'What is yes?" And "What is no?"

I know this because in 1998 when I started to learn muscle testing at a John Brimhall seminar I was one of the newbies who's head was swimming. The churning in my brain obliterated the effectiveness of my testing. Luckily, I did not give up at the point. When I went back to the office after that weekend seminar I decided to test for one thing, adrenal energy. This was an easy and effective place to start for a couple of reasons. First of all, it turns out that suboptimal adrenal function is rampant in this country due to a pathologically stressful lifestyle. The second factor that made adrenal testing an ideal place for me to start was that when the function degrades far enough it is testable by stretching any ligament in the body. Because ligaments attach joints, all that is necessary to test for General Adaptive Syndrome (GAS) i.e. exhausted adrenal

Medical Intuition and Muscle Testing:

function is to give a quick tug on any joint before you pull or push on the joint you are testing. The stretch on the ligament will make every muscle in the body test weak when GAS is present. The fact that this test is different than all of the others made it easy for me to test accurately and confidently. After I did the ligament stretch test, if it was negative for GAS, I would use an indicator point to see if the adrenals tested weak but not to the point of exhaustion that is indicated in GAS. In this way I was able to get my foot in the door of muscle testing with confidence and clarity. It also allowed me to begin to prescribe supplements, or rather supplement, because for those first few months the only supplement I prescribed was an adrenal glandular.

A few months after I began muscle testing adrenals, I took another seminar from John Brimhall. It was not quite so confusing that time. After that seminar I started testing for a few more things in my clinic and prescribing a few more supplements. The great thing about that was I still was tentative when using muscle testing, but I was helping more people more often. After that, every time I took another seminar I was able to expand the scope of my investigations because I was more clear and confident. The key? Practice makes better. As you become more confident you will find you are able to introduce the complexities of double and triple negatives into the testing. The ability to do that equals the ability to help more people more successfully.

Another pitfall to clear and confident testing is, not understanding factors that can get in the way of successful testing. Accurate testing depends on the tester and the person being tested being "clear". Being clear means the energy within flows unimpeded and interacts with the energy without. Many variables can interfere with energy flow. The place I start is with myself. I check in with myself to ensure I am clear before a day at the office. Often, whether I am clear, or not, I will do some clearing on myself. One of the clearing procedures I do is to make sure I am hydrated. Many mornings I laser the brain to make sure that all the lobes are participating.

I love knowing that I am ready to do my part as a muscle tester. The other part of the equation is the person being tested. I find out whether they are testable by touching, or focusing attention, on their glabella; the smooth part of the forehead above and between the eyebrows. For my method of testing the subject will go weak when I do this if they are testable.

42

If the subject is not testable it is up to the tester to find out why and enable the subject's energy run freely so that they will be testable. There are many methods for doing this. What I do is an amalgam of the teachings of many skilled practitioners with whom I've studied. For the system I have ordered in my energy field there are four primary impediments to accurate testability. These include the GAS factor discussed earlier in this chapter. Additionally, I find that dehydration, brain imbalance and cellular memory of emotional trauma to be the other primary factors in a subject being untestable. It is very seldom that I have worked with anyone who cannot be cleared for testing by addressing one of the four preceding factors.

There is another factor in testability called switching. A testable person has the neurological capability to exhibit coordination both sides of the body at once. This expresses awareness and coordination in the body and the brain. A switched subject exhibits neurological confusion and a lack of integration within the Extra Cellular Matrix and the nervous system that can cause the muscle tester to get false information. In my method of testing I overcome the switching problem by recognizing brain imbalance as a factor in a subject not being testable. Because my intention is searching for this before I even start an examination with muscle testing, I find the root cause of neurological disorganization/switching. I then address the root of a switched subject by balancing the brain. Once that is done I am free to pursue muscle testing without having to concern myself and the muscle testing subject with switching.

Many methods have been devised to correct switching before proceeding with muscle tests. These quick fixes are inefficient in my opinion. Although they allow a practitioner to proceed with muscle testing they do not address the root cause of switching, Often the clearing procedure must be repeated several times during the testing procedure. The most common technique I have learned and observed others using is to touch the K27 end points of the kidney meridians to test for left-right switching.

I prefer to proceed directly to the root cause and deal directly with the brain rather than have a temporary fix to the patient's lack of testability. When we take into account the existence of a Cosmic Matrix feeding into our Living Matrix and influencing our Extra Cellular Matrix we can discern that we create our

43

reality when muscle testing. I am a big proponent of this, and that is why I choose to short cut the whole switching subject by going directly to the brain.

Another way I create my own reality with muscle testing is by relying heavily on intention. At one time I used touch on a subject's body. I used a lot of vials imbued with energetic frequencies. There is no shortage of muscle testing masters who will teach you those things. Eventually, however I realized that if I believed, then I could create and utilize shortcuts. I still use touch and vials, but more often than not, I simply direct my intention. Intention can take the place of touch/therapy localization and vials. This is true because intention, like touch, like a vial with the energetic signature of the pancreas or gluten; or anything else is at its core energy. The art and science of muscle testing is and energetic conversation. Whatever props you decide to use, and intention is a prop, you will succeed when you employ confidence and clarity.

Medical Intuition and Muscle Testing:

CHAPTER 8

THE ROLE OF IMAGINATION

Imagination cannot be grasped. It can't be built. It exists on the same energetic plane as the Cosmic Matrix. It is fluid and adaptable. A predetermined path is the enemy of imagination. Time frames butt heads with imagination. The ability to travel through the world in close observation allows us to see potential in our surroundings. Potential is a precursor to excitement. Excitement is a form of the molecules of emotion discussed in Chapter 3. Apprehending those molecules helps us grasp ideas, visions and feelings then turn them around in our brain. That process may allow us to discover a different function or use for that which already exists in our worldview, in our comfort zone. Then we have the opportunity to change what we are familiar with into something more, maybe something greater and more exciting. Even if this process only happens in the mind it has produced a spark that can lead to the development of something tangible.

The concept of imagination is related to muscle testing and Medical Intuition. All three of these endeavors thrive when they escape from the busy Beta brain waves of everyday life. Calming the brain to Alpha, or even Theta waves encourages connection to the Cosmic Matrix. The Cosmic Matrix is where our attention escapes the control of the ego. Then we can apprehend the energy of the universe and allow it to work through us. In other words imagination, Medical Intuition and muscle testing all optimize their power the more we let go.

For anyone having a difficult time using Medical Intuition, or muscle testing, imagination may be a way to access the appropriate state of mind for success. The inverse may well be true also. The ability to embrace any of the three modalities is likely an indicator that you are ready to embrace the other two. All three of these endeavors share quality of the brain accessing lower brain waves. So, if you practice any of the three put yourself in a mental place where you can perform. When the energy is flowing efficiently, then it is time to switch to one of the other endeavors. Achieve the state of mind, then learn and practice the technique.

Medical Intuition and Muscle Testing:

$\mathcal{P}$ART 2:
Medical Intuition

CHAPTER 9

WHAT IS MEDICAL INTUITION

———◇———

Ethics is at the heart of human caring. It is necessary for creating the level of professionalism required of a certified professional Medical Intuition practitioner in order to operate a successful practice. Staying fully present and grounded while working with a client is a key ethical principle all professional Medical Intuition practitioners. The overall purpose of ethics is to guide professional Medical Intuition practitioners, to remain client centered, to put the client's welfare first.

A structure for an ethical practice can be broken down into 3 main aspects:

1. Client Centered- do what is best for the client

2. Develop a positive and healthy relationship with your local professional community, and the public by "speaking your truth" at all times.

3. Personal Awareness, knowing one's strengths and weakness and aligning with your highest spiritual self.

Ethical codes are conduct guidelines. They include ethics, morals, values, principles, integrity, laws and the end result; professionalism. Here's a look at how I define these guidelines:

1. Ethics, the study of morals- one's relationship to others- community

2. Morals based on culture and/or religious standards of your local community.

3. Values, a core guideline for a medical intuition practitioner is to develop according to your ethics and morals

4. Principles, are the basic code of honor that builds the framework for how you behave in your community.

5. Integrity is the ability to adhere to your principles

6. Laws are rules of conduct as set forth by your City, State or Society.

Taken together the above articles define professionalism. A Medical Intuitive is a professional when they convey the highest level of integrity to those they serve with the art of medical intuition.

There are a number of ethical concepts in the Medical Intuition profession that have developed over time to guide the certified professional practitioner (see International Association of Medical Intuitives) to act responsibly and ethically. These concepts create the foundation of ethical decision making and responsible behavior for all medical intuition practitioners. The basic considerations for a therapeutic relationship with clients are:

1. Be focused on the client at every moment of the interaction

2. Maintain a relationship of confidentiality

3. Have an appropriate professional environment if you see clients in person in office setting., The setting should be clean and provide privacy, structure and safety to the client.

4. Avoid dual relationships with clients

5. Obtain an informed consent form, before engaging in an evaluation session, or in talking with other healthcare provides of the client.

51

Many Medical Intuition practitioners work with clients long distance via phone, Zoom, Facetime, etc. Even in that setting it is important to get a client's permission before the session, or before sharing information with another health care professional.

In order to meet the criteria above Medical Intuitives must complete rigorous and extensive training. The international organizations of medical intuitives have established specific guidelines and requirements for certification. They must be met in order to become a professional certified medical intuitive. Tests must be passed to insure they have met the high standards set by the international community. At least two organizations represent medial Intuitives professionally; the International Association of Medical Intuitives, and the Global Association of Medical Intuitives, check out their web sites for yourself, don't just google Medical Intuitives, who knows what might pop on up.

A Medical Intuition practitioner can provide information on healing, how to deal with pain, adjust your diet, select treatment options, identify beneficial exercises, and improve your body systems. They can assist you to understand why your abundance is blocked, and bring clarity to your decision process. This can positively affect your healing, career choices, relationship choices and endless other decisions we make in life such as going back to school or starting a business enterprise. The clear perception of reality provided can help a person to stop projection and have less fear. The process can save lives, give hope, and illuminate solutions to a person's health concerns.

Medical Intuitives offer something that other healthcare providers and medical doctors don't. That is hope and understanding borne of clarity. This can be a placebo at worst, and a healing revelation at best. Peace of mind is important to the healing process. Too often a person returns from a visit to the doctor's office feeling depressed and confused because the visit yielded little, or no, understanding of the cause of their dis-ease. Often the objective of an allopathic practitioner is to hide, counteract or eliminate symptoms. The thing that is often left out is the "why", what is the root cause of dis-ease and distress.

When someone understands the why of their condition it can become easier to move forward. This is different than diagnosis, which Medical Intuitives do not do. They also do not claim to cure people. The insights they provide, however, can often provide a valuable insight into healing.

52

Finally, anyone call them self a Medical Intuitive practitioner. That is why we recommend you seek out a certified Medical Intuitive. There are numerous organizations that list certified Medical Intuitives. By googling certified Medical Intuitive you can access these lists and be on your way to working with someone you can trust has appropriate training in the field

CHAPTER 10

DEFINITION OF THE ENERGY FIELD

Medical Intuitives work in an unseen world that is an energy field. It is a vibrational wonder that surrounds and infuses the body. It is composed of light and information. A Medical Intuitive reading evaluates the client's vibrational signature in order to understand areas of the body, mind and spirit that need energetic attention and care. The human energy field is the person's creative universe. It is often called the auric field.

The auric field surrounds the body in an egg-shaped vibrational pattern. It is multidimensional in nature, a holographic field of energy. This energy is visible in seven separate primary fields with separate characteristics. These fields are called chakras. The totality of the auric fields contains all the information that comprises your physical, mental, emotional and spiritual selves.

All energy practitioners evaluate the energy signature of the auric field, they just do it in differing ways. The information can be used to help a client understand important matters such as their life purpose, career, romance, health/wellness and other areas of their lives.

Charles Lightwalker Lasol has spent over 40 years as a shamanic practitioner, minister-intuitive counselor, and Medical Intuitive practitioner and trainer evaluating clients. I read a client's vibrational energy patterns of the auric field. This reveals to me a person's beliefs, thoughts, emotions and

54

memories that are stored in the field. The present state of being is related to me. I see this state of being beneath the conscious presentation of a person's life. I see areas in the auric field where energy is stuck or inhibited. Those are the areas that negatively affect health and well-being. It is in that personal space that is the creative universe of potential is revealed. This potential may be physical, emotional, mental or spiritual. This information can be relayed on to the client to help them unlock that potential. It can help them to control their personal space and protect themself when others invade, or infringe upon, that space.

As a client becomes aware of their auric field, their personal space, then they can better create healthy boundaries. They learn to extend and retract their energy. The authentic full potential is allowed to flower and grow. A person's actions become authentically their own, rather than being buffeted about by the energies of others. The better a person becomes at this the better they will live the life that fulfills them and makes them happy.

As this process develops, it develops because we become in touch with our intuition and learn to access and trust it. Our intuition allows us to see and read auric fields, ourselves and others. When we observe and listen to the energy emitted by our auric field our actions become more authentic, more honest. The more honest we become, the more we escape fear, denial and victimization.

The auric field is the window to the soul. It is a window that reveals a reality that is universal, and often very different from our conscious ego created reality. Intuition allows us to see the bigger universal reality of the Cosmic Matrix. The conscious mind often attempts to clutter the view, often with negativity that can block the clarity we crave in life's pursuits. If you wish to fulfill your life's purpose here on earth a Medical Intuitive can help you by putting you in touch with, and clarifying, your auric field.

Many of the clients I have seen over the last forty plus years have limiting beliefs that cause them to wander off the path of fulfillment. Most of us were raised in an environment of mothers, fathers, preachers and teachers that have programmed us to some extent. Often the programming contributes to us becoming less than, less than our full potential. Often, we accept other's beliefs in an attempt to fit in, be part of a group. Too often, what we learn from others holds us back.

A Medical Intuitive can help people develop intuition to guide their self-awareness to realize when they have strayed from their highest calling. When we are guided to contact a higher state of awareness we can break the bonds, many formed in childhood that suppress our true self. Then limitations begin to melt away, potential and dreams reveal themselves. The world is then on its way to becoming probabilities, not just possibilities.

The intention and attention that our intuition can expose us to, can allow the infinite information of the Cosmic Matrix to feed our auric field and guide us. Change becomes possible, even when confronted by decades of old debilitating beliefs. This is the gift a Medical Intuitive can provide. When this happens a person will see more clearly who are their helpers in life, and who is holding them back with the imposition of an incongruent belief system. Then it becomes easier to let go of the influences that do not serve your higher purpose and leave room to replace them with your own beliefs.

All of the old information is stored in your chakras. The good news is that there is always room for new beliefs. With the help of energy practitioners we can strip away layers of old destructive belief systems. Each chakra is an aspect of our life experiences. Each chakra needs to have freely moving energy or our full potential is blocked. Once again intuition is the key to access and recognition of the energetic state of a chakra. A Medical Intuitive can help anyone access the information and energy of their chakras.

We have choice, even when we do not recognize we have a choice. Life events can restrict the flow of energy in our chakras. But we can also use the intuition we learn to access to turn life experiences into positive learning opportunities, opportunities that propel forward. A spirit moving forward cannot be energetically stuck. This is a simple law of physics. Keep higher energy flowing through an auric field in order to channel it out into the external world we experience. With practice and the help of a Medical Intuitive the auric field can be the catalyst for positivity and personal power, rather than a storehouse for negative life-sucking energy. It is always a great time to claim personal power and create the life you deserve.

Definition of the Energy Field

Medical Intuition and Muscle Testing:

CHAPTER 11

THE HISTORY OF MEDICAL INTUITION

The history of Medical Intuition in the healing arts is a bit shrouded in mystery. Undoubtedly, some of the ancient healing traditions of ancient Greece, the Middle and Far East tapped into the intuitive process. Certainly indigenous tribes worldwide have called on their intuition and unseen powers to assist their healing efforts. Even the Judeo-Christian tradition had prophets who connected to intuitive guidance. The term Medical Intuition, though, had little or no relevance to those early practitioners. It wasn't until the 1960's that the term Medical Intuition began to be integrated into current western healing communities.

It may be difficult to know with certainty when and where the term Medical Intuitive was first used. What is known is that the foundation for Medical Intuition is ancient, This history, though, focuses on the modern visionaries of Medical Intuition beginning in the 18th century. It ends with current day visionaries who have created organizations, worked on research, founded schools to teach the art of Medical Intuition and certify professional Medical Intuitives.

The work of Anton Mesmer, (1734-1815), in the 19th century introduced the use of intuition into the medical field. Mesmer, an Austrian physician, developed a healing technique called "animal magnetism" or Mesmerism. His healing practice became one of the first to use hypnosis. It is believed this practice was guided by his intuition and the use of hypnosis to diagnose patient's conditions and needs. A British physician, James Esdaile, followed up on Mesmer's work. He used Mesmerism as hypnotic anesthesia during surgery

A 19th century British physician, John Elliotson (1791-1868), put his patients into a trance-like state as a method of clairvoyance to enhance his medical decision making.

Perhaps the practitioner from the 19th century who did the most to bring link the use of intuition in medicine in the western world was Phineas Parkhurst Quimby, (1802–1866),. He used the terms intuition and clairvoyance in his writings. It is believed that by 1854 he was known for his intuitive healing practice. Dr. Quimby, used his clairvoyant faculty to access phenomena and information not available to the five senses. He would sit with the patient and place his mind upon them. This allowed him to exist in what he thought of as two states at once, natural and clairvoyant. The mixture of his feelings and the patient state of mind and thoughts allowed him to understand the patient's troubles and see appropriate remedies. He used this technique to amass a history just as allopathic physicians ask questions of their patients. Quimby, according to his writings in *Quimby's Complete Writings (3:210)*, used the information he gleaned to access the patient's mind and turn a patient's fear of their disease into a belief that there nothing to be afraid of with the disease.

Edgar Cayce (1877-1945), the Sleeping Prophet of Virginia Beach, brought the practice of Medical Intuition to a new higher level in the western world. His uncanny ability to asses a person's physical, mental and spiritual condition; then make a diagnosis without a history, physical examination, or any kind of lab or visualization studies has become legendary. He is reported to have made between 8,000 and 30,000 health and wellness readings in his lifetime. He was not only able to diagnose patients, but even treat them. At times he treated even when the patient was not in his physical presence. His readings often demonstrated the link between manifestation of illness, both physical and mental, and the buried emotions of the person being read.

Cayce's incredible depth of concentration turned his intuitive abilities into, what for him, were concrete visualizations of the location of disease and

Medical Intuition and Muscle Testing:

illness within the body of the person he was reading. He amazed patients and observers with his detailed diagnoses and intuitively produced suggestions for remedy.

Cayce was the transition between the old and the new worlds of Medical Intuition. This is especially true of the "modern" western world, where allopathic practices have flourished, often at the expense of historically effective, and even ancient, healing practices. The major evidence of his importance is the Association for Research and Enlightenment (A.R.E.) in Virginia Beach, Virginia; founded in 1931 by Cayce. It opened in 1928 as the Cayce Hospital of Enlightenment then was transformed into the A.R.E. The campus has become home to The Edgar Cayce Foundation, Atlantic University, Cayce/Reilly School of Massage, and A.R.E. Press.

The A.R.E. is an absolute abundant stockpile of holistic healing/medicine information. These resources are available to the public in what may be the largest source of metaphysical information in the world. Their website, https://www.edgarcayce.org, lists the following available research subjects from his readings: "Holistic health, dreams, intuition, ancient mysteries, ESP and psychic phenomena, meditation and prayer, spiritual growth, life purpose, and more."

They host conferences and workshops that pass on the vast wealth of knowledge developed by Cayce. Here, one can find tools for personal empowerment and healing that will enhance anybody's understanding of Medical Intuition. For anyone with an interest in Medical Intuition, tours of the A.R.E. Foundation vault are available by special advance appointment.

Cayce opened the door for many of the Medical Intuitives of the 20th century. J. B. Rhine (1895-1980 was a professor of parapsychology, the study of mental phenomena not explained scientifically by the psychology of his era. His work included hypnosis, telepathy, clairvoyance, intuition, and psychokinesis (the ability to move objects by mental focus alone). He began studies on metaphysical subjects at about the same time as A.R.E. was established

Dr. William McDougall created the Parapsychology Laboratory at Duke University in 1930. He invited Dr. Rhine to join him there. Mesmerism had enhanced public interest in metaphysical phenomena at that time. The scientific community was eager to study psychic and paranormal experiences. Under Rhine's leadership the field of parapsychology expanded and became clearly defined. The expansion brought the subjects of clairvoyance and psychokinesis to public awareness.

In the thirty-five years that the Laboratory was at Duke, many words we associate with the paranormal were defined and explained, including extrasensory perception (ESP), telepathy, psychokinesis, pre-cognition, and clairvoyance. Rhine was primarily concerned with ESP and worked to develop tests for clairvoyant ability. The most famous being the Zener card test. He wrote extensively about the connection between intuitive abilities and life skills

One of the most notable current Medical Intuitives is Caroline Myss, Ph.D. Some claim she is the one who coined the phrase Medical Intuitive. She started doing readings in 1982 and has done thousands of medical intuitive readings. She founded the metaphysical publishing company, Stillpoint Publishing, and worked as an editor. That platform helped her gain visibility and popularity in the metaphysical community. The result was she became the most influential Medical Intuitive of her era.

Her collaborations and consultations with holistic doctors further enhanced her visibility.

Most notably she worked with Norman Shealy, M.D. Dr. Shealy is the founder of the American Holistic Medical Association. His interest in Medical Intuition helped expand the boundaries of acceptable thought in the allopathic field. Their partnership led to the publishing of several books; *Why People Don't Heal & How They Can, Anatomy of the Spirit, and Creation of Health.*

Myss tapped into her experiences as a Medical Intuitive for subject matter she used to author several books in the 1990's and just into the 20th century. These books expanded public interest in the areas of energy medicine and healing. She began with the 1996 release of *Anatomy of the Spirit: The Seven Stages of Power and Healing,* which created a map of the human energy anatomy. *Why People Don't Heal and How They Can* and *Sacred Contracts: Awakening Your Divine Potential* followed. By the turn of the century she had transitioned from performing private readings to teaching others the practice with workshops, seminars, radio shows and more. The Caroline Myss

61

Educational Institute (CMED) was founded in Chicago, Illinois in 2003. She is a highly sought after speaker on spirituality and mysticism with her lectures taking her across the globe. She has had a profound influence on the field of Medical Intuition.

An associate of Carolyn Myss, Marilyn Parkin, PhD, is a medical intuitive, and founder of the International College of Medical Intuition in Vancouver B.C. Her time in the field of healing started innocently enough. She attained degrees in Sociology and Psychology and practiced in the field of nursing for many years. She earned her PhD in Energy Medicine through an innovative program designed by Dr. Norm Shealy and Dr. Caroline Myss.

Her International College of Medical Intuition was founded in 2002. It has pushed the field of Medical Intuition forward with its certification of numerous graduates. More can be found out about the school at http://www.mmedicalintutive.com

Another interesting contributor to the field of Medical Intuition is Dr. Barbara Brennan. Her physicist career at NASA helped her develop some novel, pioneering, and comprehensive viewpoints on the fields of Medical Intuition, energy healing and human transformation.

She developed what she calls the Brennan Healing Science. It is a holistic healing modality based on the linking of the human energy field and consciousness. This work incorporates the chakra system into its metaphysical framework. In 1982, she founded the Barbara Brennan School of Healing to teach her method. Students there develop extraordinary perception skills in a hands-on technique setting. This allows them to interact with a client's energy field in a deeply intuitive way.

It is easy to find out more about Dr. Brennan, her technique, and her school. She is a bestselling author of numerous books on the human energy field and realms of human consciousness.

What follows is a less than comprehensive list of Medical Intuitives of relevance in current times. Many on this list have founded their own schools t further the spread of Medical Intuition.

Dr. Rita Louise is a Naturopathic physician and Medical Intuitive. She travels and lectures worldwide, and is the chairman of the International Association of Medical Intuitives (www.medical-intuitives.net). She also has a training school for Medical Intuitives & energy healers, and offers some free online training introductions. She is also the author of numerous books.

Shannon McRae, PhD is a medical intuitive for almost 50 years writes for Well Being Journal. She is also the author of *The Healing Effects of Energy Medicine, Memoirs of a Medical Intuitive*. She is also a public speaker, consultant, and vibrational healer.

Winifred Adams is a Medical Intuitive, singer, master healer, author and radio show

hostess of; Making Life Brighter. She has been instrumental in increasing public awareness of Medical Intuition. She formed the Global Association to bring together Medical Intuitives to create a hub of knowledge and certify schools that can educate the next generation of professional Medical Intuitives.

Carmel Bell is an Australian Medical Intuitive and Vice President of the International Association of Medical Intuitives. She oversees a medical intuitive training school in Australia. Her work with leaders in the Australia's healthcare industry has served to bridge the gap between the use of medical intuition and the standard healthcare community. She has a training program to provide the knowledge required to become a certified professional Medical Intuitive.

Robin Eagle Sage is a medical intuitive, massage therapist, energy healer and author. She also runs a training school for medical Intuitives She has also served on the International Committee on ethical standards and training for professional medical Intuitives worldwide. Robin has also served on the Board of Directors of the International Association of Medical Intuitives and has been a leader in bringing medical intuition to the healthcare community in the United States.

Christel Nani is an RN and PhD, and author. She worked for 16 years as an ER and Trauma nurse in New York City's emergency rooms. She now teaches and lectures in Europe and the USA on the principles of spiritual responsibility. She is the founder of the Center for Spiritual Responsibility in Southern California.

Lesley Phillips, PhD is a medical intuitive in Canada, who also operates a Medical Intuition school. She is the author of *Intuition and Chakra*. Dr, Phillips has been teaching and practicing intuition for over 2o years now- https://drlesleyphillips.com/.

Lindsay Bil and Tammy Price are medical intuitives living in Canada. As certified Medical Intuitive Instructors they offer training in the field as well as private sessions for people with health concerns. They created "Shifting Into High Gear" which is a mentorship training program. The supported curriculum offers students the opportunity to study in a supported and structured environment. The linear 4 module program is available online and supports intuitive development. Lindsay is also a member of the International Association of Medical Intuitives.

There are a few allopathic physicians who double as Medical Intuitives. They combine their conventional skills with intuitive abilities. Judith Orloff MD is a psychiatrist who suppressed her empathic gifts during medical school only to reclaim them when she finished her residency. Psychiatrist/behavioral neuroscientist Mona Lisa Schultz, MD. PhD has used her academic background to draw interesting correlations between psychological literature and the chakras. Her work attempts to make scientific sense of ancient teachings about the metaphysical energy centers of the body.

In total it is evident that the field of Medical Intuition is growing. It will continue to grow and thrive as the planet evolves. Times of flux invite the greatest growth and our world is emphatically in a current state of flux. Science and metaphysics are moving closer together, and the field of Medical Intuition is a perfect proving ground for the resultant evolution of knowledge. The knowledge gained will be instrumental in the transformation from a sickness society based on the misinformation of confirmation biased "science". It will provide avenues to meld intuitive gleanings with science in the creation of a wellness society based on optimum function of the human body, spirit, and soul. A focus on function rather than disease allows humans to return to a place of healing, creating, and adapting based on the laws of the Universal Intelligence of the Cosmic Matrix.

Don't try to comprehend with your mind. Your mind is very limited. Use your intuition.

CHAPTER 12

METHODS TO ACCESS MEDICAL INTUITION

———◆◇◆———

Many types of healthcare practitioners use Medical Intuition, this is especially true in the holistic health and wellness areas. No matter who is using Medical Intuition it is their energy that dictates the results. Put another way, we all have access to the Cosmic Matrix of Universal Intelligence. It is that field that holds all of the insights a Medical Intuitive receives. Thus, you. me, anyone; from a general practitioner, MD to a shaman to a person with no title or degree can access the information needed to be a Medical Intuitive.

One of the authors, Charles Lightwalker Lasol, combines Medical Intuition with reiki. He is a Byosen Reikan Ho reiki master. He searches for disharmony or dis-ease in the client's auric field. Disharmony creates a resonant energy dissonance in the auric field of the client that he senses using his Medical Intuitive powers. Some Reiki practitioners sense through their hands, others through their unseen senses. They may sense an emotion, a thought, or even just an auric field vibration. Every disharmony on the physical level also exists on more subtle levels and that is what the reiki practitioner senses.

Lightwalker Lasol believes any Reiki Master can become a certified professional Medical Intuitive. A survey conducted by the International Association of Medical Intuitives (a worldwide professional organization) found that 85% of the practicing medical Intuitives in the association are Reiki Masters. In today's world of healing and complementary care, the more tools a practitioner has the better the client is served. The best tool is a deep understanding of the client's health and their energy field, physical body, emotional health and spiritual health. That is what Medical Intuition provides. Further, Lightwalker Lasol has observed that medical doctors, nurses, chiropractors, naturopathic physicians, Oriental Medicine Doctors, acupuncturists, massage therapists, yoga instructors, tuning fork therapists and more improve as practitioners when using Medical Intuition.

Medical Intuitives access the Cosmic Matrix of Universal Intelligence in many ways. Many use guides on their way to understanding clients, Spirit guides are one such a tool of access. A spirit guide is a western spiritualism entity. It is a spirit that has passed from living to the other side. After death the spirit continues to exist outside the body. From that detached position it can serve as a guide and protector to a living human being. The Medical Intuitive often can communicate with the spirit guide to glean information about their client or patient.

In the metaphysical world angels are guides who can focus a Medical Intuitive's insights into their client's lives. Angels are supernatural beings found in various religions and mythologies. Abrahamic religions often depict angels as benevolent celestial beings who act as intermediaries between God or Heaven and humanity. Other roles of angels include protecting and guiding human beings and carrying out tasks on behalf of God.

Abrahamic religions often organize angels into hierarchies, although such rankings may vary between sects in each religion. Often those angels receive specific names. Gabriel and Michael are examples. Some receive the title of seraph or archangel. Some have also extended the use of the term "angel" to various notions of spirits or figures found in other religious traditions. Angels expelled from Heaven are referred to as fallen angels and have no connection to Heaven. An entire branch of theology was derived to study angels. It is known as angelology.

Medical Intuition and Muscle Testing:

A channeler is a person who taps into a source outside of their own auric field, body and conscious mind in order to convey thoughts and energy from that source. Many Medical Intuitives channel in order to gather information about their clients.

Channeling is another method of accessing the Cosmic Matrix of Universal Intelligence. It is a phenomenon where the Medical Intuitive in a subconscious state aligns energetically with the with an outside energetic source. The outside source provides information to the channeler who serves as a voice for the entity they are channeling. In essence the Medical Intuitive acting as a channeler allows the entity to use the medical Intuitive's mind, emotions, and vocal cords. The information provided may then be useful in the process of understanding a client and giving them direction toward greater health and wellness.

A Medical Intuitive will often use breathwork and visualization to access spirit guides, angels or animal totems. Animal totems are a big part of Native American spirituality. They are symbolic representations of another type of spirit that can be used as a guide by a Medical Intuitive. Animal totems may be represented by inanimate objects. These include the totem pole, as well as types of jewelry such as talismans. Talismans are usually an inscribed ring or stone. Some traditions believe every individual has an animal totem. Accessing your totem allows entrance to another realm with greater connection to universal wisdom.

A telepathic link to spirit guides, angels, channeled entities, or animal totems is a great way for a medical Intuitive to help their client.

Chakras are another valuable tool for Medical Intuitives. The chakra system originated in India over 2500 years ago. The story of chakras is found in an ancient Indian test called the Vedas. The basic human chakra system is commonly accepted to consist of seven chakras. These start at the base of the spine and end on top of the head. Chakras are a complex network of energy channels, equivalent to a spiritual nervous system connecting all areas and aspects of the body. Chakras are perpetually in motion along the human body's spinal column and each has a unique vibrational frequency. The most common chakra system has seven chakras. It is a basic system, and a more complex system exists that introduces several more chakras. The seven chakras are associated with specific parts of the body, yet they are not physical entities. They exist in realm that in eastern mystic lore is the "subtle energy" realm. The subtle energy realm is a crossroad of the material and the immaterial, the biological and the spiritual. The body, mind, and spirit meld together in the subtle energy realm.

Their names, locations and colors of the seven basic chakras are:

Root chakra — base of the spine — red

Sacral chakra — just below the navel — orange

Solar Plexus chakra — stomach area — yellow

Heart chakra — center of the chest — green

Throat chakra — base of the throat — blue

Third Eye chakra — forehead, above between the eyes — indigo

Crown chakra — top of the head — violet

The eighth chakra is the point where the soul of a person merges with the Cosmic Matrix of Universal Intelligence. Here is where the soul manifests as physical matter of the energy body. The eighth chakra helps one see their life as a spiritual journey disguised as a physical experience. This is reminiscent of the famous saying that, "we are spiritual beings in a physical body".

Reading the chakras can be a fantastic tool for a Medical Intuitive. Opening the third eye chakra can enhance the ability to access one's guides, thus tap into the power of your intuition. Understanding the chakra system allows a Medical Intuitive to interpret the condition of their client. The chakras are catalysts of consciousness and human function. They govern various emotional issues, from our survival instincts and self-esteem to our ability to communicate and experience love. They can show unbalanced areas of the energy body that may contribute to a lack of wellness, that is exactly the kind of information that can set a Medical Intuitive apart form an allopathic practitioner.

We focus on healing the whole body by activating and balancing our chakra system through bringing awareness to the location, sensations and the influence that our emotions have on our chakras.

Others intuitives have used the Channeling Quartz Crystal to deepen their access to universal wisdom. The Channeling Quartz Crystal is a highly

Medical Intuition and Muscle Testing:

distinctive configuration of a seven-sided face at the center front position and a triangular face on the opposite side of the crystal. The seven-sided crystal face represents precision within the intuitive realm of a higher mind, and analytical understanding in the mental and physical bodies. It symbolizes the student, the professor, the mystic, and the seeker of wisdom.

The three- sided triangle on the opposing side provides for creative and innovative verbalization of inner truths. It represents both prerogative and the power of speech and the ability to both creatively and joyously express self.

In this configuration, the seven represents the accessibility of innate wisdom and the three represents the ability of manifestation and verbal communication. The combination represents initiative and the independence between the world of the physical self and the perfection of universal wisdom.

The Channeling Crystal guides the seeker into the expression of truth and wisdom obtained from the inner realms of the perfection of the Cosmic Matrix. It helps to provide a conscious connection to the higher wisdom of experience and enlightenment of the hidden world. Some Medical Intuitives use Channeling Crystals for meditation, to seek answers to specific questions, and even access the stored information of the record keepers. It is very important to remember that we have access to all of the knowledge we seek.

Yoga means union with a supreme power that is the source of creation, perfection, and destruction. The Cosmic Matrix is a vibrational energy that is the source of creation, perfection, and destruction. Yoga has been practiced for thousands of years and is rooted in Chinese medicine philosophy and martials arts. In yoga a combination of meridian and chakra exercises, healing sounds, meditations, breath work and visualizations are used to facilitate awareness in and of the Cosmic Matrix.

Some intuitives use vibrational yoga to channel their intuition. In vibrational yoga a strong yang practice is accompanied by breathing techniques and yin yoga. Often there is an additional modality of sound incorporated to raise vibrations to an even higher level. The vibration focuses attention to cultivate the abundant energy of the Cosmic Matrix. As the body releases energy blocks and cultivate the life force energy of the Cosmic Matrix intuitive abilities expand. The resultant merger of the core self with an intuitive state prepares the Medical Intuitive to assess and assist their clients.

A human being is a small universe. When the consciousness of that small universe unites with the energy prevailing in the vast canopy of the Cosmic Matrix the union is complete, and the light of wisdom starts flowing in the human body. The light contains everything a human need to evolve. A human as a part of nature is constantly striving for perfection. This is the natural course of evolution because the Cosmic Matrix is the personification of ultimate perfection.

Vibrational yoga puts practitioners into the flow of the universal force that is the Cosmic Matrix. It helps to achieve the balance that is the key to the power of nature, to find the balance between two extremes. The Universe is composed of seemingly extremely contradictory forces, day-night, sun-moon, man-woman, good-evil. Yet, one cannot exist without the other. Even hectic and tortuous paths eventually achieve a truthful balance.

There is no textbook or short cut to self-realization, but the techniques listed in the preceding paragraphs can help us achieve the vibrational state necessary for the Medial Intuitive. They are methods to invite the truth and love of divine guidance from the from the Cosmic Matrix into ourselves. That guidance flows spontaneously to and from the person who is tolerant, patient, humble, fearless, confident, spreads happiness always, and has speech full of love and compassion. Such a person becomes a perfect channel for the energy of the Cosmic Matrix.

Much of all disease is caused by mental and physical abuse. Abuse causes a lack of balance in the Extra Cellular Matrix that distorts the Living Matrix and distances humans from the Cosmic Matrix. The human body has built in remote controls for all mental, and physical ailments. The controls, however, depend on balance in the three matrices. The Medical Intuitive learns to operate those controls in order to restore balance in a distressed body.

It is the work of the Medical Intuitive to find the imbalances in their own being and in others. Imbalance can cause the accumulation of toxins in the body. These toxins can be removed with a thorough cleansing. The

71

methods in this chapter help to detoxify the body and regulate vibrations, thus channeling our life force towards spirituality. Balance in the mind body, make it more receptive to the universal life force pouring from the Cosmic Matrix. It is advised that medical Intuitives have some grounding practice they do daily.

Remember always, whatever is sent forth on the waves of thought and deed in the universe will always come back to us. Our miseries, sorrows, and disease are all results of our deeds. Our world is the creation of our thoughts. We sometimes blame others or circumstances for our failures and miseries. But our mind is a product of our environment, deeds and worldly education. When knowledge of failure is bred is interference in the matrices of life that stops the innate flow of consciousness.

The Cosmic Matrix is the source of everything we need. The job of a Medical Intuitive is to clear the interference of educated conscious mind. We all progress at our own pace that is dependent on the awareness we cultivate. A daily practice helps to ensure that development of awareness and spiritual goals. The potential exists to evoke tremendous strength and power of the mind when linked to the Cosmic Matrix. Then intuitive powers can produce a Medical Intuitive guided by the supreme source. Everything is possible and there are no coincidences in life and it is available to all.

The more communication there is with the Cosmic Matrix the more life force for the spread of love, truth, and light avails to us. As that life force expands so does the beauty of the world. Things fall into place. The heart fills with truth that the whole world is family, all of one source, sparks of the same light. The joy of being a human being is realized. Abundance and gratitude flow from the auric field and permeate all they contact. This Medical Intuitive who achieves this state will be immensely successful.

This chapter has explored much of what has been written on the paths of enlightenment and enhanced intuition. There is an abundance of knowledge available to us. Volumes have been written by many learned scholars; the libraries are full of them. Now the circle of time is turning, exposing wisdom for all who care to expand consciousness and intuition. This is wisdom that transcends religion. It is there to prepare us for a new age where conscious awareness of the Cosmic Matrix will guide the evolution of people toward success, perfection, total bliss in the form of love for all.

CHAPTER 13

MEDICAL INTUITION RESEARCH – WHO GETS TO DEFINE IT

———◆◇◆———

Science holds a revered position in the modern world, especially in so-called advanced cultures. Humans exist as a species that highly values certainty. With doubt comes fear. Consequently, we humans search for concrete answers. Often, we cling to answers because change creates the possibility that what we have might somehow be diminished by change. Ironically, this is often true even when what we have is not really what we think we have and/or what we really want. The fear of losing something is often greater than the prospect of gaining something better.

Many authors, psychologists, philosophers and others have written about the five stages of grief. Those stages are generally determined to be denial, anger, bargaining, depression and acceptance. Those stages are applicable to much more than human response to grief. Anything that causes monumental change in a person or in a culture, often has to go through the five stages.

Perhaps the battle for acceptance is more difficult in the arena of science than anywhere else. Science in the health and wellness field is especially resistant to change. The media often leads the anger and denial charge in the face of new scientific knowledge. This is due to the oligarchical nature of our government. Oligarchy means that corporations dictate what happens politically in the U.S.

One of the seven corporate entities that dictates the direction of policy is the field of health, dominated by the pharmaceutical and insurance industries. Media is another. They are apparently enabled to direct policy because they influence politicians with monetary contributions and expensive favors.

If and when favor is curried from politicians it allows the insurance and pharmaceutical industries to set the ground rules for the health and wellness field. The ground rules claim that only proper research can be used as evidence for any method or modality. Yet, allopathic medicine, the practice of drugs and surgery, is not held to the same standard of proof of efficacy as "holistic" modalities and professions. A definition of science is, *"a branch of knowledge or study dealing with a body of facts or truths systematically arranged and showing the operation of general laws",* courtesy of dictionary.com.

When the definition is broken down the inclusion of the word study precludes any scientific branch from being static. From the Oxford Dictionary, *"the devotion of time and attention to acquiring knowledge on an academic subject",* indicates a never-ending search for the truth. Too many people, including scientists and politicians, like to claim that science is some static entity that cannot be contradicted.

The irony of this is that science must be open to evolution to be science! Unless scientists study the subject, it is not science. History has shown us that when a subject is studied discoveries will be made. Those discoveries can challenge the truth as we know it. Science, by definition, needs researchers to challenge scientific opinion, even if it deconstructs an opinion.

Still, many people view science as the unquestioned truth even though change Is an integral part of the field of science. Too many times even the scientific, religious or political community is highly resistant to change. There are multiple examples of this in history the most well-known, classic example is Galileo. In 1633 he was persecuted for publishing a treatise on his observation that the earth revolves around the sun. For that observation he lived out the rest of his life under house arrest until death in 1642. He was an extreme example of what can happen when those at the top are in the denial or anger stage of a change to their profession, discipline , or belief system.

Medical Intuition and Muscle Testing:

The allopathic medical field has a long history of trying to eliminate holistic modalities with the federal government as its ally. The denial, anger, bargaining, depression and acceptance progression reared its ugly head with my profession, chiropractic, in the 1970's and 80's. A lawsuit saved chiropractic from going the path of osteopathy. In 1967 osteopaths caved in to the American Medical Association (AMA) and began the conversion of all osteopathic schools to MD granting universities. In 1987, after 11 long years in courtrooms, a federal judge ruled in chiropractic's favor in an antitrust suit against the AMA. Chiropractic survived, only to slowly have its philosophical roots slowly eroded by insurance companies and within the profession.

Many chiropractors, nutritionists and other types of healers went to jail for practicing their professions in the early to mid-1900's. Many were victims of the blind arrogance of the allopathic profession headed by the AMA. These are illustrations of the allopathic profession's refusal to grant an equal playing field to professions that threatened them. The AMA positioned itself to be the arbiter of whether other healing professions satisfied the requirements of research driven evidence of their efficacy. Far too often the allopathic field has remained in a state of denial, no matter what evidence was presented. Ironically, in these cases, the Johnny-come-lately allopathic profession was allowed to pass judgment on methodologies that pre-dated the drugs and surgery model by up to thousands of years.

Science must not be allowed to be a matter of cherry-picking whatever research and evidence supports a hypothesis. Instead it needs to be a self-correcting methodology where all the evidence is considered and critiqued. Science should be a field where competing hypotheses are tested. Many research projects and books masquerade as science, but amount to little more than speculation and polemical propaganda in support of a preconceived belief. Sociology has a derogatory term for this, confirmation bias. We are currently living in an era of extreme confirmation bias that has created an atmosphere of fear. That fear has allowed health care agencies and politicians to direct health care in a restrictive manner that eliminates constructive criticism and discussion. In other words propaganda has replaced science.

There are specific parameters that exist to separate real science from fake science. Quality research must embrace reliability and validity. They are the

76

indicators of the accuracy of test methods, techniques and test measures. Reliability is the consistency of a measure, and validity is about the accuracy of test methods, techniques and test measures.

The gold standard for research is the double-blind placebo controlled peer review study where neither participants nor researchers know who is receiving a particular treatment. Placebos are utilized to prevent researcher bias. The identity of those receiving a test treatment and placebo is concealed from both researchers and participants until after the study is completed.

The tragedy of our current system is that many will be fooled by authoritative sounding books and "scientific' papers. Often, we choose to look at only one side of the data and the result is that we think there is "proof" where there is only the anecdotal evidence of experience that lacks scientific basis. Scientifically naïve readers will be convinced, critical thinkers will not. A prime example of this is prominent in the Covid-19 response. In the initial months of the "Covid pandemic" doctors found that some pharmaceuticals reduced symptoms, kept people out of the hospital and kept them alive. Two drugs in particular were found to be effective: Ivermectin and hydroxychloroquine. They were highly discouraged from being used by the AMA, CDC, WHO, FDA. They were labeled experimental because they had no researched track record with Covid. They both had been in use for many years with a very safe track record in terms of side effects. Doctors who prescribe, and prescribed, those medications have been harassed; despite saving lives and keeping their patients out of the hospital.

It is common in the U.S. to deny permission for an already approved drug to be used for other conditions before approved research studies are performed for another condition. This, though, is not a hard and fast rule. Given the backlash to the use of "experimental' medications for Covid, it is reasonable that the same criteria would be applied to the new Covid vaccines. For some reason, though, the mRNA vaccines were fast tracked into distribution without the depth of research normally required by the Federal Drug Administration of the United States. This is an obvious double standard, and a double standard that likely contributed to an exorbitant number of deaths.

Covid has exposed the weaknesses in the United States healthcare system to a greater degree than ever before. Ask yourself, how does the supposedly most

Medical Intuition and Muscle Testing:

prosperous nation on earth with a population smaller than many other countries end up with by far the most COVID-19 attributed deaths? Health insurance restrictions and bias toward experimental vaccines, and away from "experimental medications" are at least partially to blame for the inflated death rate in the U.S.

When there was an urgent need to expand testing and treatment for COVID-19 health insurance appeared to often be in the way. The federal government has felt it necessary to subsidize hospitals to attempt to ease the covid burden and the backlog of surgeries and medical care it created. The administrative waste and inefficiency created by an exorbitantly costly insurance sector appears to have further contributed to the death rate in the U.S. The lesson to be learned is to look deeply, both within and without, into any subject you wish to understand better. We all would have been better served to do this with the current state of medical research in the U.S.

Critical analysis is especially important with a comparative analysis of Medical Intuition and allopathic medicine. We have allowed our health and wellness world to become populated by flimsy erroneous "research". The has produced a health care paradigm that is followed blindly. The result is disease and death characterized by the overuse of pharmaceutical medications and surgery.

The allopathic field is a landmine field of failures and lack of research. The result is that one of the most prosperous nations on earth, the United States is also one of the least healthy economically developed nations on earth! A group that calls itself Organisation for Economic Co-operation and Development (OECD) was formed in 1961. It tracks all elements of economic progress including health care in its 38 member countries.

In most of the member countries infant mortality rate has improved. For the past 50 years the United States has not kept pace. The average for OECD countries is 3.8 deaths per 1,000 live births. In the United States it is 5.8 per 1,000, ranking 33 out of 36 countries. The only state in the U.S. that meets the average is Massachusetts at 3.8 deaths per 1,000.

OECD also tracks obesity prevalence which has been increasing over the past three decades in the United States. Using self-reporting, nearly a third of the

United States population has a body mass index above 30.0 categorizing them as obese. Thirty-three other OECD countries utilized self-reported obesity data. Of these the United States ranks last. The highest ranking U.S. state, Colorado would still rank next to last if it was a country. The OECD average is 16.7%. This is extremely important because obesity is the leading indicator of chronic lifestyle disease and related deaths.

Life expectancy is another OECD ranking. It is an indicator of how long a newborn can expect to live on average if current death rates remain the same. The United States life expectancy at birth of 78.6 years ranks No. 28 out of the 36 OECD countries, The average life expectancy in OECD countries is 80.7 years.

For decades the United States has spent more on healthcare than any other country. And, it's not even close! Pharmaceutical medications are many times more expensive than in other countries as are hospital and physician visits. In the United States the average person spends almost double on pharmaceutical drugs than what any of the other most prosperous country's citizens spend. Surgical procedures can be many times more expensive than other countries yet there is a low life expectancy and a high suicide rate in the U.S. According to OECD statistics, in 2018, the United States spent 16.9 percent of gross domestic product (GDP) on health care, nearly twice as much as the average OECD country.

In spite of all our medical system failures, medical intuition is not universally offered to clients by most health care providers; nor is it paid for my health insurance carriers. The allopathic world will argue that Medical Intuition does not meet research requirements. That statement ignores the gross willful lack of adherence to the rules of research by the allopathic community. Those rules are deemed good for holistic interventions, but easily overlooked in pharmaceutical studies.

As a result, many people have never heard of Medical Intuition, and don't realize how it can help them with their health and wellness concerns. For a Medical Intuition evaluation to become a routine and widely available health assessment tool for assisting clients in understanding their health issues its benefits must be scientifically established as **evidence based**. That will necessitate preliminary studies to determine the feasibility, required time, cost

79

and risk of adverse events involved in this research. Clinical trials need to be designed with large numbers of subjects.

Medical Intuition research studies are most likely the only way to convince medical and healthcare providers, as well as health insurance companies, to invest their time and money in Medical Intuition as an adjunct to health care providers such as Acupuncturists, Chiropractors, Medical Doctors, Psychologists, Naturopaths, Reiki Therapists, Yoga Therapist and other others. But even before these research studies can begin, we must bring together the current leading edge Medical Intuition schools, teachers, and Certified Professional Practicing Medical Intuitives worldwide and standardize the industry. Standards allow certification that will inspire confidence in the public. The many schools cited earlier could be part of a global effort to create a worldwide certification process and an association to take Medical Intuition into the future. The certification process could differ from school to school and still cover the basics of energy healing,

"I would rather go to my grave enduring the struggle against medical ignorance and prejudice, than for the sake of acceptance suffer the indignities of medical subordination."

Fred Barge DC May 1995

81

CHAPTER 14

SUPPORTING YOUR INTUITION

————◇————

For all of us, or maybe just most of us, who aspire to access a stronger connection with the Cosmic Matrix of divine intelligence it is necessary to put forth effort. Most of us inhabit a hectic world that seeks to activate the ego and suppress the intuitive connection to the Cosmic Matrix. For that reason it is recommended to get in the habit of activating intuition as many times a day as necessary. Grounding is good word for that kind of activation. Among the tools the two authors have utilized over the years are meditation, visualization, affirmations, diet, yoga, exercise We have both utilized healing modalities such as chiropractic, Oriental Medicine, Healing Ki Way, massage and many more modalities.

The objective is to stay grounded to keep energy flowing freely within the Cellular Matrix and the Living Matrix. Then any person can increase awareness of internal and external environments. That grounded state affords greater opportunity to access the infinite knowledge of the Cosmic Matrix. Then any person, including a Medical Intuitive, can transfer that energy to others in need and help them release their physical and emotional pain. The more in tune one Is with the Cosmic Matrix, the more effective that person will be in any healing endeavor.

A positive attitude is helpful if not essential to all holistic healers. Positivity is an outgrowth of connection to the Universal. That connection is an outgrowth of the diligence and effort applied to develop connectivity. That is why we recommend some form of daily practice to enhance grounded connection to that which is greater than us. The Medical Intuitives initial presentation sets the tone for the rest of the interaction. A presentation of positive thoughts and beliefs can be the placebo called hope for those who seek help. Hope is often the springboard to a successful practitioner/client interaction. As the esteemed now deceased chiropractor Fred Barge DC once proclaimed in an On Purpose interview, "Ahh, the placebo, the only drug to withstand the test of time."

Medical Intuition and Muscle Testing:

CHAPTER 15

MY JOURNEY, CHARLES LIGHTWALKER LASOL

"I honestly believe to be a great Medical Intuitive, you must be clear within yourself and free from negative influences. You need time and ample space for yourself, your personal healing. And always create good boundaries and realize the client must want to heal themselves for your evaluation to work."

Charles Lightwalker Lasol

Intuition is the gut feeling one has when logic is taken out of the picture. We are born with intuition; however we often learn to disregard it by a culture that devalues it. Often we are taught to use the conscious mind for all decision making. Yet intuition is always present beneath the conscious surface. Some have the good fortune to have been encouraged to develop their intuition. Then the possibility exists for a life in the flow of messages from the universe.

In that state a person can be guided on life's journey by a higher power. Medical intuition is the process of using that guidance to focus on the health and wellness of a person. That focus, combined with tools such as understanding energy fields and muscle testing can produce accurate in-depth evaluations of a person's health and wellness. Medical intuitives see where imbalances that can cause illness and disease exist, where a body, mind or spirit needs attention. They can help to formulate a plan of action to bring a person back into balance. Observance of energy fields, chakras, organs and other body systems can produce a clear picture, for the medical intuitive and the client, of the path back to wellness.

My path began as a teenager. I was not the kind of student who always studied enough. I found I could use my intuition on multiple choice tests and do very well. During a test I would quiet my mind, read the question an let my intuition provide the answer. I passed a lot of tests using that approach. I began to trust my intuition to tell me what classes to take in college, what jobs to submit an application, even what girl to ask out at other times. I wasn't always so good at the last one.

I began to condone intuition with meditation to help with bigger decisions. At times while in the US Army my intuition told me to question authority. When I talked back to my Sergeant, he got mad and told me I was not to be allowed to take a training class I had already been qualified to take. My intuition told me to go over his head and apply for the position. I did apply and was transferred to a different unit, just before my previous unit was shipped to Vietnam.

Another time I was injured while on duty. The Sergeant told me to suck it up and to not complain. Luckily, I followed my intuition, went to the doctor and discovered I had a serious injury. It took several months of rest and light duty to repair the damage that had been done. I would never have gotten the chance to heal if I had not listened to my intuition.

As I matured, I came to understand that intuition is a gift. Used correctly it provides insight and understanding. It can be the source of a super power escape from the rational mind of logic and ego. Time progressed and intuition guided me toward healing methods that fit my skillset. Learning was easy because I was being guided to areas where I could find and use my passion. When I use Reiki intuition tells me where to send energy. The same with tuning forks, intuition guides me to the correct tuning fork and placement of the vibration. When to use the tools of my shamanic healing work is entirely guided by intuition. Even when performing ceremony intuition guides the protocols I follow.

Most importantly, intuition can be used in daily life as a guide flow with ease. That allows for greater insight and understanding. It allows us to see the depth of that exists beneath the surface of all things.

A medical Intuitive evaluation of a person's health can help to determine what lies beneath the surface. To heal it is necessary to view the roots of illness, energy deficits, imbalances and confusion. Then solutions for wellness become clear. I have seen thousands of clients, and many find profound relief when someone finally tells them that there are solutions and they are not crazy. Reflect on the sense of relief you would feel when someone finally tells you, "No, it's not all in your head." This offers the client the opportunity to take control of their condition and begin to access their own intuition and make better healthcare decisions. Some of my clients have become inspired to the point they decided to become healers. They have gone on to become Reiki masters, Massage Therapists, Medical Intuitives and other certified healthcare practitioners.

Intuition opens the door to a more empowered and directed life filled with passion and meaning. For me it has been the gateway to expanded knowledge and my spiritual roots. It allows my soul to shine through every day as a husband, father, healer, teacher, author, volunteer in veteran's programs, board member and more. I encourage everyone to allow intuition to help free you from the bonds of mundane daily life.

With discipline and persistence, I believe, anyone can open their intuition. It can be a discipline of self-love and respect that surrenders to a greater wisdom. You will be amazed at the results when you expand your intuitive nature. And, if you have health concerns don't hesitate to enlist the aid of a Medical Intuitive. If you are already a healthcare provider, consider facilitating your own Medical Intuition in order to better help those that see you professionally.

"It is through science we prove, but through intuition that we discover".

Henri Poincare

My Journey, Charles Lightwalker Lasol

Medical Intuition and Muscle Testing:

CHAPTER 16

MY JOURNEY PATRICK DOUGHERTY DC

I am one of those people who had a vague awareness of the hidden world as a child. There were things I perceived and did not understand. Initially, I had an unwavering trust in grownups to explain the inexplicable. Over time I let go of that trust. One of my early memories, before I was even ten years old, was hearing sirens. This happened with a high degree of frequency. I would ask where the sound was. The answer was always some variation of, "I don't hear anything." Unfortunately, I appeared to be the only one who heard them. I was so certain of the existence of the sirens that I convinced myself that something was being hidden from me. A grain of mistrust was sown.

Another series of incidents had to do with seeing pictures in books that were totally familiar to me despite the fact I was supposedly seeing them for the first time. Most of the time it was pictures from the orient that triggered the recognition. No matter how many times I asked adults for an explanation of this phenomena there was never a discussion of the topic.

Sometimes I noticed that I knew something was going to happen, just before it happened; or I knew what someone was going to say before they said it. Memories of asking for an explanation of this are coupled with memories of my questions being dismissed. Sometimes I would want to pair colors because they looked good to me. The piano could produce sounds that pleased my ear, yet I was told the sounds and the color combinations were wrong.

As an inquisitive child I frequently wanted to know, "Why?" Far too frequently, the grownups I wanted to trust ignored my questions or answered with, "Just because.' I Wanted to be able to trust those with more experience, and supposed knowledge, than me. Doubts crept into my mind. Somewhere along the way trust dissolved. Lost faith in adults eventually was coupled with lost faith in the ability to access, or even believe in, a world beyond the five senses.

By the time I had graduated high school a significant degree of resentment, and doubt, permeated my psyche. Lost faith in authority figures helped to create a rebellious teenager, me. I rejected far too much in order to distance myself from people I believed had proven themselves unreliable. Among those unreliable people were medical doctors. One of the areas in my life that suffered during that period was attention to my health. I smoked cigarettes and my diet became almost devoid of real foods. After a few years of this I found myself in a cycle of cold or flu, sinus infection, chronic bronchitis, antibiotics that left me ill half of every year.

It took two to three years of that cycle to convince me that medical doctors and antibiotics were a poor solution to my health challenges. Not knowing where to turn, I began to read books related to health. The first book was <u>Back to Eden</u> by Jethro Kloss. That was instrumental in starting a slow conversion to better food choices. The second book I found was <u>The Web That Has No Weaver</u> by Ted Kaptchuk. It is a book about Oriental Medicine and it was the beginning of a revelation that there were alternatives to the allopathic field.

I had stopped smoking after about three years and had begun to eat better, but the cycle of illness remained. I decided that I would find an Oriental Medicine Doctor and get healthy. It was 1974 at that time and I was living in Denver Colorado. We had phone books, not computers, in those days so I opened the Yellow Pages and went to acupuncture. To my surprise there were only two Oriental Medicine Acupuncture Doctors in the entire Denver metro area of 1.167 million people. That figure is a good indication of the state of holistic energy medicine at that time.

Medical Intuition and Muscle Testing:

One of the doctors was in Denver proper, the other in Boulder 25 miles down the 36 highway. I chose Dr. Lee in Denver. He was more than twice my age, gruff and not too communicative; but I chose to put my faith in him. I found ways to come up with enough money to see Dr. Lee, initially three times a week, and buy herbs from him that I had to turn into a tea that I drank several times a day. This lasted for many months before frequencies were reduced. The cycle of illness continued, but I noticed that I was not sick for as long as previously when the cycle would start. I continued treatment later in Chinatown San Francisco after I moved. After a few years I still got sick at least once a year, but it lasted only a few weeks rather than a few months.

It took about a decade before I had a year without contracting a cold or flu. That was a huge deal for me. During that decade I continued to read alternative wellness books whenever I found them, and I began to see chiropractors. What I had come to realize is that the books I was reading and the practitioners I was seeing had philosophies and practices that addressed the unseen energies – the power that made the body heals the body. The world of insight into Medical Intuition was opening up to me, but it took many more years before I could put a finger on that pulse.

By 1984 my longtime chiropractor, Dr. David Sanders of Wheat Ridge CO, had talked me into going to chiropractic school. Though I had about 100 college credit hours they were too eclectic to get me into chiropractic school. After a couple years of travel and establishing residency, I began to accumulate the required credits for getting into Chiropractic school. I lived in beautiful Fairfax California while attending College of Marin and Sonoma State University. That took another couple of years. Finally, in 1989, I was ready to enter Western States Chiropractic College in suburban Portland Oregon. I left the San Francisco Bay area about two weeks after the devastating 1989 Loma Prieta earthquake, one of the more memorable events of my life.

I began studies at Western States in late 1989. The curriculum was very dry and there was almost no mention of chiropractic philosophy which is very metaphysical. I struggled through 39 months of chiropractic education in order to be able to become a healer. When I graduated, I soon realized I was a mechanistic technician, not a healer. I started a business but closed after a year. I spent three years working in a clinic that specialized in treating auto injuries. I learned many things, but not how to help people help themselves.

In 1998 I went to a seminar where Dr. John Brimhall DC was the main presenter. That was the beginning of a wonderful opportunity. Over the next 6 years I went to numerous Brimhall Method seminars. That is where I was introduced to muscle testing, and where I first saw that chiropractors could move beyond a mechanistic practice. Thus began a slow evolution into the doctor I am today.

After ten years of practice in Denver CO I had become stuck in all elements of development. That led to a move to Spokane Washington in 2004. I moved mostly blindly, but I had a feeling it was the right move at the right time. The move turned out to be a huge factor in the development of my awareness of the hidden world and how to access that world.

In Spokane in 2005 I fell in with a group that wanted to form a Holistic Chamber of Commerce. In Denver I had organized a couple of holistic fairs for alternative practitioners. I suggested our chamber do the same. There was some resistance, but I insisted that I would put on a fair, with or without the assistance of the chamber. In the fall of that year the first Spokane Holistic Chamber of Commerce fair took place in the downtown Community Building sponsored by KYRS, a local nonprofit radio station. It was a big success, but it also fractured the chamber causing several people to withdraw from the chamber.

My biggest ally in putting on the fairs was Charles Lightwalker Lasol. He was well connected in the area holistic community. I left it to him to find fair vendors while I dealt with the nuts and bolts of the fairs. We continued to put on two to three fairs a year, steadily growing, through the fall of 2012. The fairs were instrumental in the development of my wellness philosophy. I met so many brilliant practitioners with so many brilliant philosophies and techniques who furthered my understanding of what intuition and healing could be.

I have never been one to stand still in many facets of life. I held on to lessons from many of my friends and colleagues from our fairs. Those lessons became parts of how I practice chiropractic today. I use tools introduced to me by fair participants. Wonderful conversations expanded my awareness of how to use the tools I do use. Without the knowledge shared with me by so many others I

91

never would have developed my style of muscle testing. That style has, over the years, led me to rely on, incorporate and fold into the field of Medical Intuition. Alternatives to mechanistic practice are there to grasp I have learned. There may always be a mechanistic aspect to what I do, but practice consistently astonishes me when the patient and I plunge into unforeseen areas. The need for a plan can fade away because the Cosmic Matrix is always available to us via our Living Matrices. We ask and are guided to places the thinking brain is unable to access. That is the essence of Medical Intuition. It does not matter whether I use muscle testing, or simply see into the great unknown. The point is to see beyond the conscious mind, using any tool we can.

Finally, nothing stays the same. My practice is a constant evolution, always incorporating new ideas and techniques, moving closer to an ideal relationship with the Cosmic Matrix. The same can be said of Medical Intuition. It constantly shape-shifts. New people are involved, new ideas. Potentials are vast and I believe largely untapped. But as humans tap into that potential, then healing experiences will expand. Those healing experiences may be on an individual world, or they may be the experiences needed to rescue a planet from human destruction, from wars, hunger, genocide. It will be impossible to sustain much of what humans are doing on this planet if the masses tap into the infinite knowledge of the Cosmic Matrix. What sometimes seems so far away can flip in a seeming instant. That is the lesson of what Malcom Gladwell termed the Tipping Point. The knowledge is there, waiting for us to shut down the ego and seek guidance.

Good luck to all who pursue that path.

93

BIOGRAPHY

Charles Lightwalker, PhD

- Founder/CEO, Center for Intuitive Studies

- Founder/CEO, Charles Lightwalker/Metis Medicine

- Certified Medical Intuition Instructor,

- Certified Spiritual Healer,

- Shamanic Healing Practitioner and teacher,

- ordained Minister and Certified Religious Counselor.

- founder and CEO of The Center for Intuitive Studies, presenting educational programs for professional and personal intuitive development.

- Charles's accredited certification program, Medical Intuition Practitioner ™, has been pivotal in helping complementary, and holistic healthcare professionals from every discipline to develop and optimize their innate intuitive abilities, to serve humanity.

- Charles received certification as a Spiritual Healer, and was ordained a minister from the Spiritual Healers and Earth Stewart Congregation in Spokane

Washington, Charles also is an acclaimed shamanic practitioner

- Master degree in Chaplaincy Studies, from ULC Seminary

- PhD in Religious Studies From Newport University.

- founded Center for Intuitive Studies in 2010 to present his unique educational programs in health, wellness and Metis Medicine ways. The company reflects

\-   Charles's mission to share shamanic and spiritual wisdom with cutting edge healing tools to provide and education experience that creates powerful practitioners willing to embrace wholeness in each client so they can truly heal.

Printed in Great Britain
by Amazon